ROADS WE'VE TAKEN

A Writers on the Avenue Anthology

Pearl City Press
MUSCATINE, IOWA

Publisher's note: Names in nonfiction essays have been changed at the author's discretion.

Acknowledgements: "Keeper of Her Memories" first appeared in the collection *Heart Songs* by Mica Rossi

Cover design by Kaitlea Toohey
kaitleatoohey.com
Book layout ©2017 BookDesignTemplates.com

Roads We've Taken / Writers on the Avenue -- 1st ed.
ISBN 978-1-7369498-5-6

To all the scribblers, from childhood on

And to my son, Aaron, for his unwavering support of all of my humble endeavers.

Tom Hogue

Contents

CAROL J. ANTHONY

Release

In a nest of nature
we wrap you.
Vestiges of dog fur
mingle your bones.
You lie on a bed of
Spanish moss
magnolia leaves
pine needles.

A fir cone
steadies your ash.
Trailing ends
tie the knot.
You are beautiful,
Man of the Arts.

Your nest is gently placed
as if putting the baby down.
The Black River
envelops you.
Lingering for a bit,
you change color
to brilliant orange gold—
as if an ember.

1

Bits of you trail out
dissolving in black tea.
Sinking, you send us
tannin bubbles.
Formations of
cluster
string
heart.

You are gone.
Free, where you
wanted to be.
You returned
to Lowcountry—
your childhood sea.

Photo: Carol J. Anthony

BOB BANCKS

My Green Plymouth

Every young man remembers his first car or pickup truck. It's a sign of being a man and not a kid anymore. You own something.

When I turned sixteen, my mother and I rushed to Muscatine's courthouse to get my driver's license. Although I'd been driving for two years with a driver's permit and had several years of tractor-driving, I was a nervous wreck.

The highway patrol officer walked with me to our family's big blue Pontiac. For some reason, I'd locked the car before I took the test, which was rare in the 1950s. I was so nervous I couldn't get the key to work. The officer was patient and told me to try again. Heck, I had the key to the trunk and not the ignition key. I unlocked the car, reached across the seat, and unlocked the passenger side. We drove for about three blocks and back to the courthouse. When I parked, I pulled ahead too far and was not lined up with the parking meter.

The officer said, "I believe you are not in the proper space."

I backed up and shut the car off. I figured I had failed. The officer wrote on his clipboard and handed me a slip of paper.

He said, "Congratulations. You're a good driver, but next time, watch where you park."

I thanked him, presented my paper to the lady inside, and received the precious license. For the rest of the school year, I drove the big Pontiac for school activities and dances. I was quite popular because most of my friends were much younger than I was. I still had to ride the school bus to school since Mom needed the car during the day.

The next summer in 1957 my older sister, Mary, became engaged to be married. She had a teaching job and needed a more reliable mode of transportation than her new husband's car. My mother decided to buy the couple a new vehicle as a wedding present. The couple went car shopping and found the perfect two-door Chevrolet. When Ron, my sister's husband, offered his auto as a trade-in, the salesman told him it was only worth $99 and that he should try and sell it himself. Ron was dejected. After all, it was a green 1949 Custom four-door Plymouth sedan with only 80,000-plus miles. I had no car, but I had $99. I bought Ron's Plymouth and I had my first car.

It was reliable with its flathead six-cylinder engine and stick shift. Now, if you are not familiar with this engine, it means all the spark plugs sat on the top of the engine block and not on the side. The stick shift meant you had three gears forward plus reverse. You changed gears with a clutch. It had an AM radio, wool fabric seats, and disc hubcaps on the wheels. The tires were black, not the fancy whitewall tires of Mom's Pontiac. Air-conditioned cars were for the very rich; a Plymouth owner wasn't offered such a luxury.

The first thing I did was to polish it until the car shone like a mirror. With a couple of hours of elbow grease and a can of Turtlewax polish, it was a dark green shining jewel. The car paint of the 1950s was not as good as to-day's, so, I had to polish twice, maybe three times a year.

The best thing was I had wheels. When high school started in the fall, I could drive instead of riding the bus. I could stay after school for activities and still get home for chores. Most of all, I was independent of my mom.

By the end of that year, many of the guys in my class turned sixteen. Most had cars much fancier than my Plymouth. Ford introduced the Fairlane and Crown Victoria. Chevrolet had the Impala and Nomad. Plymouth introduced the Fury with its high tail fins. Power and V-8 engines were in. You customized your car if you were good with motors and other car amenities. Chrome hub-caps with star-shaped spinners, whitewall tires, dual ex-hausts, and four-barrel carburetors feeding the engine with cheap gas were the norm. If you ever saw the play or movie *Grease*, that's my era.

Since there was no possibility of upgrading my Plym-outh with its six-cylinder engine, and its owner was al-ways strapped for cash, my amenities included just two things. I installed fake whitewalls called Port-o-Walls be-tween the rim and tires and a chrome exhaust diverter that was nothing but an ornament.

The only problem I had with my car was that when I drove through fog or a light mist, moisture would collect around the spark plugs on top of the engine and short out. Soon the engine would start missing and losing power.

One evening, after I had taken a date home, I was on a road with dips and hills. The dips were filled with fog and the dampness caused my engine to misfire and lose pow-er. I would barely make it to the top of the hill, then the spark plugs would dry and the engine purred. I thought I would never make it home. As I drove up and down the undulating pavement, the Plymouth misfired in the dips, then dried out on the hills. I was close to my uncle's house, so I thought, "I'll just pull into Uncle Jim's and borrow his car. I can get my car tomorrow."

As I approached Uncle Jim's, the fog miraculously lifted. The engine dried out, and I never had to wake Uncle Jim or borrow his car.

In the winter I installed tires on the rear wheels with an aggressive tread that could plow through the snow. When spring came, I changed back to regular tires. One spring night, I hadn't had time to change my tires, so I was still riding on the mud-snow tires. I had two other classmates riding with me as we cruised Second Street in Muscatine. At a stoplight, we were challenged by another group to a game of car tag. It was a fun challenge I knew I would not win. The other driver had his dad's huge Chrysler New Yorker. Yet somehow my buddies and I were in the lead. We tore around town and were close to a section where a tree nursery was located.

One of the guys in my car, Gary, said, "Turn in here. We'll ditch them in Walton's Nursery."

Although we were trespassing, I pulled into the maze of lanes in the nursery. The big Chrysler followed.

The lanes or paths were all dirt. I had an advantage because of my higher ground clearance and my mud-snow tires. We drove through the nursery until we hit an area where the owner was watering his trees. I didn't slow down and plowed through the mud, while Gary looked out the rear window.

The big low-slung Chrysler hit our muddy ruts and sank into the mire. We exited on the other side of the nursery.

Gary yelled, "Slow down! Turn here!" Then he started to laugh. "Charlie is stuck in the mud. I can see his car. Boy, is his dad going to be pissed!"

My Plymouth may have gotten muddy, but it proved it was a good mudder.

On a Friday night in July of 1958, my Plymouth registered 99,998 miles on the odometer. I was in Muscatine cruising with a couple of pals.

One said, "Let's drive around until you hit one hundred thousand."

So we drove up Second Street and down Third Street in Muscatine until the odometer started to turn. At the stop light on Iowa Avenue and Second, the meter started to roll over. By Sycamore Street the bottom of the 0 started to appear. Finally, when we drove one more block to Cedar Street, the full 100,000.0 miles could be read. We all cheered. It was almost midnight, and every hangout was closed. There was no place to celebrate. I drove my friends to their homes and continued to my place near Blue Grass. By the time I parked in the machine shed, the odometer read 100,018 miles.

Now the good part of all the cars of the '50s and '60s was the front seat had no console in the middle. Seat belts were not required until the mid-'60s. This meant your girl could ride sitting right next to you. There were times the girl rode so close to her boyfriend that from the back of the vehicle they looked like a two-headed person. If you had an automatic transmission, you could drive with one hand on the steering wheel and the other around the girl's shoulders or, if you were romantic, her knee. Unfortunately, with a stick shift, you had to shift with your right hand, so no extra petting was allowed.

I drove my Plymouth until November 1958. I had accumulated some extra cash from my 4-H projects and work. I would be going to junior college the next year and needed a more dependable vehicle. The '59 models were arriving, so dealers were anxious to sell their leftover

'58s. I decided to buy a new car. I bought a brand new six-cylinder, straight-stick 1958 Chevrolet Delray for $3,000. It was another bare-roots car with no air or fancy radio, but with its Blue Flame engine spark plugs located on the side of the engine, it was much more dependable.

Once again, the dealer didn't want a 1949 Plymouth for trade. I put a free classified ad in our electric company's newspaper. I sold my wonderful green Plymouth for $100. I made a dollar and a lot of memories. My 1949 green four-door Plymouth Custom Deluxe sedan with fake whitewall tires gave me freedom to roam, independence from the family auto, and access to a high school social life that included girls. Especially the girls.

More Room

One dollar got me forty minutes of parking on Washington Street in downtown Iowa City. It was a lovely spring day. I stopped there on my way home from Ames where the youngest of my four children, Beth, has two summer jobs before continuing graduate studies at Iowa State.

Six years ago on a hot August day, I sat on a stool in this same spot at the front of this shop. I held my cup of cappuccino over a white saucer and looked out the window. Angled spaces were gone in favor of parallel parking. I felt like God had smiled on me to find a spot near the Java House next to Englert Theater. Then, as now, the sun was bright in a cloudless blue sky. A group of students with whole lives ahead of them sat at an outside table, sipping their coffee, wearing shorts and Birkenstocks.

Six years ago, Beth was beginning her freshman year at the University of Iowa. Her father and I had moved her to Slater Hall in the midst of all that freshman move-in-day chaos. Lots of parents waited in line for the elevators. Again, as with the many move-in-days of her siblings, we hauled boxes up flights of steps. Within a couple of hours we had her bunk made up, clothes unpacked, photos pinned to her half of the bulletin board, and a note left for a roommate she had yet to meet. The three of us drove downtown to Garden Market for lunch. College towns are full of hope and vitality along with new construction that seems always in progress. There was so much to explore, and we'd have four whole years to do it. This youngest child was beginning a new chapter in her life, and I was reluctant to let her go.

Looking back, I'm reminded of a quote by Elias Canetti: "One lives in the naive notion that later there will be more room than in the entire past."

I put my cup and saucer in the bus bin, walked to my car, and drove east on Washington to Governor Street. It's a one way that turns into Highway 1 North. It took me past the apartment Beth rented her senior year and the Hy-Vee where we bought groceries together. I merged onto Interstate 80. Fifty minutes later, home. I pulled into the gravel driveway of our big old farmhouse. For the first time in 35 years, none of my children will be living at home for the summer. They are fun and interesting people, and I miss them.

My husband was not home from golf league. Our neighbor, on his tractor, stirred up a sweet fragrance raking hay in the pasture east of our barn. Beth used to keep her horses in that barn. As I walked to the house, I saw a dove sitting on eggs in one of the flower boxes. Mowgli wagged his tail, pleading for attention. I patted his shaggy head, faced the house, and wondered what to make just two of us for dinner.

MIKE BAYLES

In the Telling of a Story

Eric looked out the window of a back room as he searched for the missing part of the story he was writing. Light peeked through clouds as they drifted through the sky. Sparrows danced in the yard, but their chatter was muted. His thoughts returned to Ellen, his ex.

His chest was heavy as scenes played in his mind of moving out of his ex's house five months ago.

Plodding footsteps echoed through the family room, and the door creaked open. Virginia, a former classmate from high school, stood in the doorway. "What about integrity?"

"I'm writing," he answered, while an unfinished page flickered on the computer screen. "For a creative writing course at the community college."

Virginia was letting him stay and help straighten out her house after he moved back to town, so he could find an apartment and a job to start his life again. He only had until the end of summer.

She crossed her arms. "It wouldn't be a crime to give me a hug."

He got up and wrapped his arms around her while holding his breath. She smelled of sweat, and she had let her appearance go since they were in high school five years ago. As he pulled away, she puckered her lips.

"No," he said.

"You've only got a few months to stay. What are your plans?"

"Heck if I know." He shuffled his feet. "It's hard when the biggest part of my life was taken away." He pointed at the screen. "I'm trying to get it back."

He hummed a song and looked around the room.

Virginia frowned. "It must be Ellen."

"I'd give anything to see her."

"Go ahead and go back to her. Let her kick you out onto the street again."

Eric sighed. "Maybe we can get it right this time."

"Is it her or me?"

Ellen was in a band and just divorced when she and Eric got together. They kissed and danced, and they started seeing each other. And after he graduated from college, they had a long-distance relationship.

He closed his eyes as if reliving the scenes.

Virginia nudged his shoulder. "But what about me? The one who's putting you up."

"And I thanked you." He shrugged his shoulders, and she pouted. "What can I say? I told you that we'd never be more than friends."

"And what about her?"

"I was saying one thing, and her father said she needed a husband in her life, and I thought he meant me, but she ended up saying something else."

"So, is that the story you're working on?'

Eric nodded.

She glanced at a stack of greeting cards, envelopes, and a pen.

"You wrote to her again?"

Eric nodded, and her face grew red.

"I better go for a ride," he said.

Cars driving the other way downtown passed in slow motion. He felt as if he were someone else looking down on his life. He wondered what he was doing there, in a small town. His life was in slow motion.

He was living and dying for Ellen, memories finding new life in the story he was writing, but with each draft, the ending was the same.

If only I could explain things to her, he thought. His mind filled with the words he left unsaid, a dialogue longing to be on the page.

A frail woman carrying shopping bags crossed in the middle of the block, and he slammed on his brakes. She didn't look at him. In the park, carefree children danced, and music played.

A canal for horse-drawn barges stretched along the north end of town. Water leaked from a broken lock, and the canal bore its time. Large leaves of lily pads floated on the surface like open hands. The sun shone, but his shoulders drooped, burdened by thoughts.

A man in a tattered shirt stared as Eric waved his arms, acting out dialogue of his piece.

"It's a story I'm working on."

The man turned and walked away.

But a voice still called out to Eric. He figured that he could finish the story by the next week. That would be the easy part.

He walked and he walked and he walked in shadows of his dreams as he pulled a letter out of his pocket, one that said she had found someone else.

MIKE BAYLES

Townsend

I am the reflection of early light
on still waters in a clearing
just outside of town.
I am a morning stilled.
I am the vision
of people walking
the cabins as they hug
the lake's shores.
I am soft conversations
visions of a friend sought
while we're both on the road
working our jobs.
I am the whisper
of a great forest
and the wonders
of animals wandering
in thickets of undergrowth.
I am recollections
as I move place to place.
I am a journey without end.
I am heartfelt memories
of those I've known.
And now
sitting in a quiet room
I lose myself
in reflections of time.

DEE CANFIELD

Loafers

"Mother, it's almost time!"

I turned on our television console with the 12-inch screen, and as the black and white static receded, I began to adjust the knobs for better reception. The image of a glass of fizzing Alka Seltzer appeared, flickering and rolling, and I continued tuning until it settled on the screen. In a few minutes it would be time for "I Remember Mama," the show starring Peggy Wood as the gentle mother of a Norwegian immigrant family in San Francisco. I was 12 and I loved to imagine that I was one of her children.

"Can you watch it with me?" I asked.

"Does it look like I have time to watch television?"

My mother was ironing in the kitchen that adjoined our small living room—the only downstairs rooms in our two-floor apartment in the Arsenal Courts, the housing project in the west end of Rock Island where my mother, my two younger brothers, and I lived.

Mother took in ironing and some days she ironed 12 hours a day. A Pall Mall cigarette hung, stuck on her bottom lip, and it wobbled as she brought the iron down hard and fast on the board. She frowned in concentration as hot steam sizzled on the cloth and drops of perspiration formed on her forehead. She made quick work of the shirt: first up and quickly back down the placket, the side on which the buttons were sewn, then the button-hole side; then the collar, the cuffs, the sleeves, the back of the neck, the back of the shirt, and finally the two front sides. Then she placed her cigarette on the ashtray, wiped her forehead on her sleeve, hung the shirt on a hanger, and put it among the ranks of starched items hanging from one of the long, narrow water pipes near the ceiling in our mustard yellow kitchen.

My mother and father had met when he was stationed in England before shipping off to Normandy in World War II. After the war she and I came to the States to begin our new life with him, but he was institutionalized from the time I was eight until I was 18. His heavy drinking and bursts of anger had terrified me. In my adult years I came to sorely regret the loss of his presence in my life, but as a child I felt such relief with him being gone.

My father had served in four major military campaigns; his unit had been awarded four Bronze Battle Stars and he personally had been awarded a Purple Heart. No one understood PTSD in those days, and it wasn't until I was well into my adult years that I put two and two together. How could someone survive four major military campaigns without having inward scars? His traumatic experiences in the war brought about the change that, in addition to taking his life in a tragic, unexpected direction, dashed my mother's dreams and changed all of our lives forever.

I don't understand how it was that she smoked continuously and yet the clothes always maintained their freshness. And although it was difficult for me to breathe when I was in proximity of the smoke, to me the worst thing was the ashtray full of cigarette butts. Just looking at it filled my mouth with an acrid taste, and when I walked past I always gave out a long, soft, silent exhale because inhaling at that moment would mean that I would somehow be taking the ugliness into myself.

"Dolores, try on those dresses that Mrs. Harris left."

My mother's customers not only brought their weekly ironing, but also occasional hand-me-downs which my mother would take in or let out so that I could have some new clothes. I took the load upstairs and began to undress.

"Well?" she called from downstairs.

"I don't have one on yet."

"Hurry up and don't dawdle!"

My mother was a quick worker with a quick wit, a sharp tongue, and not much patience. She walked fast and laughed hard and had little sympathy for a 12-year-old dreamer who couldn't ever seem to move fast enough. I was constantly reminded that cleanliness was next to godliness and our house was always in spotless order. Unfortunately, invading cockroaches were always attempting to mock her standards. Our housing project had been built on a swamp and the insects had a longer history in the place than humans. But Mother was quick with a shoe, and she employed every weapon in her arsenal to establish our territorial rights.

Mother taught me that there was a right way to do everything, including the dishes: always, always the glasses first, then the bowls, plates, silverware, and pots and pans last. And every dish had to sparkle. I understood that there was a right way; unfortunately, I seldom achieved mastery over any task because I couldn't make things clean enough or do the job fast enough, and usually she would tell me to "leave it" so she could "do the job properly." And if I avoided tasks altogether, I would be scolded for being lazy or, what was apparently worse, always having my nose in a book.

The first dress was a matronly dark brown gabardine. Fortunately, my mother let me decide which ones I would keep, and I tossed it onto the floor. The next dress was a sleeveless cotton print with a pointed collar and a full circle skirt. The pink, blue, white, and yellow stripes ran vertically in the bodice and horizontally in the skirt. It was pretty, but it was a style more fitting for someone older than me. In addition, the material was somewhat faded and there were a couple of tears in the hem. However, it was something that my mother could fix, and since I had to choose something from the pile, this seemed like a good possibility. I began to put it on.

"Well?" my mother called again.

"Yes, I found one. I want to try it with my crinolines."

"Did you get them off the line?" My mother had starched my crinoline slips and hung them over an umbrella on the clothesline so, I hoped, they would stand out even farther.

"I forgot."

"You'd forget your head if it wasn't screwed on!"

I posed in front of the mirror with my hand on my hips, then turned to look at the back.

"Dolores?"

"What?"

"Go and get them!"

"I'm coming!"

"So's Christmas!"

My mother had more than her share of sayings and phrases. She was always pushing and prodding me while she herself forged ahead with grim determination on any task that lay ahead. ("The Lord helps those who help themselves.") Her life gave evidence of this determination. Her survival had depended on it. Because of grave childhood illnesses she hadn't gone much beyond the second grade. When she was eleven, she had been wheel-chair-bound, and then there had been another childhood illness, scarlet fever I think, that she hadn't been expected to survive. She was an adult during the war and she told me that, during the German bombings of Southampton, her parents' home was the only house left standing on their block. Eventually, they were so tired of running to their backyard shelter when the air-raid sirens began that they would stay in bed, listening to bombs exploding in the distance.

She was a great one for telling great stories and I felt such pride when she made people laugh until they cried. ("Laugh, and the world laughs with you; weep, and you weep alone.") And she didn't tell just funny stories. She had some exciting tales to tell as well. She told how, one night, she drank and danced with Basil Rathbone in the London Underground as bombs dropped overhead. As wonderful as that story was, I took it at face value, though of course it reflected a certain amount of daring and savoir faire. It wasn't until years later, when I saw news footage of the Underground during a bombing raid, that I realized just how extraordinary the story was. The people in the news footage were not drinking and dancing. They were huddled together in fear. But it seemed most plausible to me: if anyone would be dancing in a London bombing raid it would be my mother, Elsie.

When my mother and I came to America, we left the middle-class home of her parents and she came with a trousseau. She had a full set of silver and, for special occasions, we would reverently unwrap the knives, forks, and spoons from the maroon velvet cloth in the expensive-looking case. It wasn't until my adult years that I realized at one point that we no longer had the silver. No doubt she had sold it to raise funds for just getting by.

We lived on a very small monthly stipend from the Veteran's Administration, and my mother's ironing helped us to make ends meet. She stretched every penny; the war years and living on rations had taught her well. She made use of everything, including saving scraps of paper. ("Waste not, want not.") She wrote the current week's grocery list on the back of the previous week's receipt, which we would use as we carefully shopped at the neighborhood IGA store, two blocks away.

I went outside into the fresh air of the warm September evening. The locusts were buzzing, fireflies blinking off and on, and I could hear my brothers playing with kids in the neighborhood: "Olly olly oxen free!" I took down the umbrella holding all my starchy slips from the line, carefully removed the slips, folded up the umbrella, and carried everything into the house. As I came in, my mother was buttoning up another completed shirt. I laid everything on the kitchen table.

"Can you quit for a while?" I asked. It was time for "I Remember Mama" to begin.

"What do you think?" She waved to the tall basket of ironing in the corner. "I have the Harris's ironing to do yet. It'll be midnight before I'm done."

I wished my mother didn't have to stand there like that, day after day and into the night. She had terrible varicose veins, purple and blue, that bulged from the back of both legs, but even though standing was painful, she didn't let the pain interfere with her work. The only thing that could make her lie down and rest were the intermittent migraine headaches. I dreaded to hear that the aura had appeared, for then I knew that she would be very sick. It really wasn't fair that she had to work so hard, but I hated hearing her bemoaning that fact.

She was often reminding me of the unfairness of life

and that "other people have so much and we have so lit- tle." I felt as if everything was somehow my fault. The worst thing was that there was nothing I could do to make things right.

"Go and try on the rest of those dresses so I can get them washed and mended tomorrow." She wiped the perspiration from her forehead. Then she stubbed out the old cigarette, lit a fresh one, took the next shirt, laid it down on the board, and forcefully placed the iron on it.

"And put those slips away carefully! I don't work like a Trojan for nothing!"

When I was younger my mother was fond of telling me that children should be seen and not heard, and I had learned to carefully monitor my words. But from the liv- ing room I could hear Peggy Woods's gentle chiding of her daughter, Katrin, and I was anxious to see what was happening to my television sister.

"I'll do it later, Mom," I said, with a bit of irritation.

"You'll do it now and you won't talk to me in that tone!"

I felt her words in the pit of my stomach. The butts were piling up in the ashtray.

"Yes, mother," I sighed. With my eyes on the TV, I carried my slips into the living room to sit on the couch.

"Oh no you don't!"

"But M—om!"

"Business before pleasure! Turn it off!"

"But—"

"Now!"

Defeated, I turned off the television and trudged up the stairs. I sat on the bed and looked at the pile of secondhand dresses. I sullenly tossed two or three in a pile on the floor with the brown gabardine.

And then it caught my eye. Although it was a bit faded,

the color still carried the promise of a sky-blue summer day. It had a white Peter Pan collar, short sleeves, and, best of all, the fullest of skirts. I put my crinolines on, one by one. Then, breathless, I slipped the dress over my head and placed my arms through the sleeves, hoping it would fit. I tugged it into place and zipped up the back. The short-sleeved bodice fit perfectly and I cinched it at the waist with the wide, white belt. I twirled and watched my reflection in the mirror.

"Mom!"

"What?"

"Mom!" I ran downstairs.

"Well?"

"Look!" I ran into the kitchen and twirled again. I swung the skirt into a wide, full circle with a full, poofy bounce of the crinolines beneath.

"You'll have to change that belt."

"Why?"

"You can't wear white after Labor Day! Besides, you want to wear your new brown loafers, don't you? You'll have to wear a matching belt."

"But I don't have one!"

"Go upstairs and look in my top dresser drawer."

"Really?"

"Well, go on!"

I ran upstairs, searched, and came across a brown suede belt. I had never seen it before. It was beautiful. I put it on and then put on my new brown loafers, each with a Lincoln-head coin that my mother had carefully tucked in. They matched the belt and I imagined myself in my new outfit at school. I couldn't wait to get downstairs. When I came into the kitchen, my mother put down her iron. "Lovely," she said. And then she smiled, and I no longer needed Peggy Wood.

MELISSA CONWAY

My iPhone ran out of memory last weekend

I tapped through photos and videos, trying
to suss out what's expendable.
I don't recognize myself in photos. I make eye contact
with this flickerfaced moonbeam with my nose
my clothes, but I can't place the moments
she was living in. The bars and basements,
exes and class projects graded over.

I pause for a second at a snowy selfie I took
while skiing. Smiling next to me is a boy I don't remember
meeting, but I remember staying up too late
playing cards and pool in the dining hall with him. I flipped
through the photos of hazy parties and fast food drive-thrus
in crowded cars, movie nights backdropped in dorm rooms.

The oldest picture
I have on my phone is a selfie I took
with my middle school best friend. We were waiting
in line outside a haunted corn maze, steeped in anticipation
for the future. This was 8 years before he died. I pierced
through the cartilage of my left ear last night.
I can't let this one heal.

MELISSA CONWAY

Penny & Ed

Grey hair
high collar
thought lines
worry lines
these are Creation lines
stone-slab glasses
perched laughter
history canyoned through freckles
an artist's hands
arthritic hands
familial bruising
these are healing hands
holding hands
with her husband's
engineer hands
helping hands
white hair
stroke touched
love lines
frown lines
these are hope lines
their daughters laughing in the kitchen
lemon-foam hand soap
toffee piled in glossy blue ceramics

perched still
long long long dinner tables
carved wood lines
home lines
these are blood lines
running through me.

MELISSA CONWAY

Flood Nicotine

I'll spend my life whispering I love you until you fall asleep
candles smell better in afternoon thunder
windows half-cracked rain splashing onto your cheeks
you say you know me through half-tilted half-smiling lips

Candles smell better burning in evening rain
you always come home covered in a cloud of jasmine
you say you know me through half-splashed half-laughing lips
I keep meaning to switch from nicotine to green tea

You smell like jasmine and coffee and threshold
happiness finds a home between the curves of your hips
I keep meaning to switch from green tea to honey
I trace the momentum of your ribs kissing every freckle
every dimple

Happiness marks a home between the curves of your lips
I mark your heart with lilacs and mourning
I trace the hills of your shoulders kissing every freckle
every dimple
Everything you touch tastes like rosewater sweetening

I mark your heart with muddy hands
Windows half-cracked splashing on your freckled cheeks
Every rainwater drip of your body tastes like lost continents
I'll spend my life whispering I love you until you fall asleep.

MELISSA CONWAY

Summer Everlasting

My brother stands against the rising sun, feet swallowed in tomato vines blushing green. I see his shadow's hands shaking in the dirt. He takes a sudden step forward that arcs into a crouch. I see the top of his head shimmering chestnut, his cheeks splattered with a freckled mess, his hands outstretched claws. I see his bare feet toeing the line between tomato and a wall of cornstalks. I hear an owl call from the shed as if to say *steady now.*

Sweat drips down his sun-choked face, golden drops haloed in morning. The tomato vines look thirsty. His frame, swaying back and forth, tenses suddenly. He is still, then all at once he leaps forward with a half step, arms reaching out to the new stalks poking the sky. He screams *I got it, I got him!* over and over, struggling to pull its body loose from the roots without getting bit. I say *careful* between sips of coffee from the back porch steps.

An owl calls low from the shed. I wonder if it can see the angled sun poking through the wooden slats where the door was hammered back on after that snowstorm in '02 and then again last July. *Check it out* Bobby says, running toward me, all wrapped up in this long brown rope of a snake.

I see layers of dirt caked between his toes. I sit on the back porch steps scratching at mosquito ankles. He holds it out to me, its head pinched open. I touch its body cool and sleek and tense under my fingertips. *You gonna keep it?* I ask. Bobby just shrugs, the snake's head slipping out of his grasp, coiling up to his forearm. He panics, starts pulling the snake off and dropping it to the ground. *He's not a biter* I say, but Bobby already slipped forward and kicked the wooden beam bordering the garden. I watch the snake's lurching body escape.

I see blood turn dirt to mud between Bobby's toes, but he just laughs and watches as it slithers crookedly back toward the fields. *At least put some shoes on* I say as he hops over to the rusted green hose on the side of the house, still laughing. An owl calls from the shed as he washes his feet clean.

VICKY DOVENSPIKE

In the Attic

They lived in a dark, musty attic with cobwebs hanging from the rafters to the sidewalls. It was cold in the winter and hot in the summer. The room was filled with stacks of magazines and catalogs providing plenty of reading materials. A velvet photo album holding sober faces sat on a small table alongside an old RCA phonograph. Just above on the wall hung a gold oval frame containing a baby photograph. Who could it be? A row of cardboard boxes, heavy with dust and memories, occupied floor space. In the west corner, I remember a brown leather saddle thrown across a wooden sawhorse, a harness and sleigh bells hung from a rusty nail. A faded blue rug muffled footsteps and a floor lamp with intricate carving on the base provided evening light. Two flowered dresses and striped denim bib overalls hung on a wire rack. Four straight-backed oak chairs with broken spindles were positioned around a table. They had everything they could possibly need.

As a child I had an eerie feeling I shouldn't be there. The narrow door that led into the attic was on the south wall of my bedroom. Sometimes I heard noises, so I locked the door. Often I pushed a piece of furniture in front. I slept with a light on to scare my fears away.

The house is gone now. All that remains are trees that surrounded it, leaving me to wonder: where do ghosts go when the house no longer stands?

VICKY DOVENSPIKE

What Color Are Memories?

Blue because I miss you
Red, the color of my heart
Are they yellow
Because they warm me
Or black, because we're apart?
Maybe they're white because they're pure
Perhaps purple, regal and bold
Could be the color orange;
They give me happiness untold
I think the color green
For they flourish in my mind
Probably brown because they're ageless
Set forever in time.

JUAN FOURNEAU

Rocky 4

In the holiday season of 1985, I was in 7th grade. Twelve years old, looking forward to winter break and becoming a teenager in March. That Thanksgiving weekend *Rocky 4*, starring Sylvester Stallone, came to my hometown of Muscatine, Iowa, playing at the Riviera Theatre downtown. My older brother Jorge was the first in my family to go. I was so jealous.

All I could do was watch the music video on MTV featuring the song "Burning Heart." That was almost cool enough. The music video showed clips of the movie, whetting my appetite to watch the film. I can't remember what kept me from heading downtown to see it. Perhaps it was the money. Maybe I was waiting for my brother Ismael to take me. Or my friend Manuel Cadena to see it with me. For whatever reason, it wasn't happening.

When I did see the flick, it blew my mind. Apollo Creed dying in the ring, fighting like a true warrior to the end, was devastating. The press conference scene afterwards with the deadly Russian Ivan Drago displaying his stone-cold killer silence was intense. Bridgette Nielsen giving the Soviet Union's propaganda talking points made my blood boil! Who did these communists think they were?

The fondest memory of that year's Christmas season began by reading the movie ads from the local *Muscatine*

Journal. It advertised *Rocky 4* would have a matinee showing daily during the school break. Every day of my almost two-week break, I could watch this film for $1.50.

There was more. For an additional $1.50, I could get popcorn and soda. For $3 a day I could see this movie! In 1985, seeing a movie at the cinema more than once was a serious and expensive commitment. However, with this special holiday bargain matinee, I had a plan. My paper route money would go to this marathon movie session.

As my Christmas break from Central Middle School began, I walked downtown in the cold from my childhood home at 504 West 4th Street. First was a stop at Cohn's Newsstand to read the latest wrestling and muscle magazines. When the time neared two o'clock, I headed next door to buy my ticket. I found the perfect seat, surrounded by the gothic structure of the 1930s Riviera Theatre. As the film reels began rolling, the previews started. I couldn't wait to see Rocky knock his rival out.

What blew my mind every one of those showings was the training montages that Stallone created and put together. My favorite scene was Rocky training to "Hearts on Fire" by Survivor. In the cold, desolate winter, far from Philadelphia, Rocky was immersed in an emotional old-school workout, fueled by the burning desire to avenge his fallen friend. On the big screen it was contrasted to the high-tech, stoic, futuristic training Ivan Drago was incorporating.

The movie appealed to this young, skinny, Hispanic boy with a big imagination. I was enthralled by Superman, Bigfoot, Star Wars, and the monsters of professional wrestling. It was the 80s, and we wanted bulging biceps and explosive action in our movies. My 101-pound frame was tired of pipe cleaner arms, and I wanted muscles.

Inspired, I would race home and lift the thirty-pound concrete weights attached to a curl bar I had in my bedroom. The training was solitary and tedious. Just like the workouts Sly threw himself into in the Soviet Union to even the score against the Russian Ivan Drago.

Those *Rocky 4* training montages inspired me for decades. I still train at times to the *Rocky 4* soundtrack. If you see me pumping iron at the gym, there's a good chance that's what's blaring through my headphones. When I see impressionable young Latino teens just starting out at the local Muscatine Community Y flexing their biceps, I can't help but smile.

Years later when I became a pro wrestler, I tried to emulate those emotions when creating the conflict we were writing in the ring. The character of Ivan Drago, played by Dolph Lungren, is one of the greatest villains created in cinema. And in Rocky, America had an endearing underdog protagonist. The conflict was perfect for its time, the 1980s Reagan era. We were deep in the Cold War, and I didn't like these Russians.

I'm thankful my 13-year-old son Alex loves the Rocky and Creed series. He's surpassed me in the number of times he's seen *Rocky 4* and can quote all the memorable scenes. We enjoy watching the films together on the streaming channels of today. Movies on demand are a wonderful convenience.

But it's hard to beat the feeling of leaving your home and heading down to the local movie house. You get your hot fresh popcorn, ice cold soda pop, and grab your seat. When the lights go down, the theater darkens, and you're transported to another world. One where you're not distracted by social media or your phone while you're squinting at a small screen.

The winter break of 1985 will live with me forever. I

still carry a piece of that scrawny, impressionable seventh grader. I'm grateful for those Christmas *Rocky 4* matinee showings at the downtown Riviera Theatre and the magic they made me feel.

KATHLEEN UNGER HART

Home of My Heart

"Where is the home of your heart?"

My brother's casual question to the family gathering
falls in a sudden silence.

He is remembering childhood summers
in Schuyler County with our cousins,
ranging the hills and creeks of
our little kingdom, our uncle's farm.

Home of my heart...
my eyes flood,
scenes spin in my mind.

A scattered childhood provides
no single house
worthy of the prize

Home of my heart...

"Nineteen-sixty-three," I tell him,
      but even that is wrong.

KATHLEEN UNGER HART

Aunt Katie

When spring rains turned the country road to mud
    the school bus stopped
    at our Aunt Katie's lane.

Her brother's children from the next hill over,
    barefoot, carried their school books and shoes
    down their steep lane and up to meet the bus.

In the cool spring morning, Katie washed their feet
    with water she had warmed and carried down,
    wiping thick red clay from between their toes,
    drying them with towels she would have to wash
        and bleach
        and hang to dry,
helping with shoes and socks,
sending them clean and presentable into the world.

At Easter every year when Christ picks up
    His washbasin and towel,
    I see Aunt Katie,
    washing my cousins' feet.

KATHLEEN UNGER HART

Watermelon Memories

"Look what I brought home from Muscatine!"
Charlie rolls a treasure onto the tailgate:
    the perfect watermelon, cool, ripe and ready.
A knife-touch splits it. We all grab chunks and dig in.

As the first bite bursts in my mouth I burst into tears.
Where did that come from?
Juice drips from my chin.
I remember a Sunday School picnic
My dad, tie and suit coat gone,
    sleeves rolled up for the watermelon-eating contest,
    digging in face-first, a country boy again.
I wipe the tears with the back of my hand,
    pretending my hair is in my eyes.

Another big bite. Spitting out the seeds,
I think of Mom passing out melon
    as we crowd around the big oak table.
My brother tells his wife, "Move that way just a little,"
    but that would put her out into the yard.
The look she gives him! We laugh 'til we can't breathe.

Charlie hands around some paper towels.
I wipe my face, eyes, nose, hiding my tears.

I lift the melon to my mouth again and see
    my father-in-law, eyes shining
    with love and joy at having surprised me
    by changing his plans to show up at the reunion,
    offering me a slice of watermelon
    like a special present, as indeed it was.

"Here, have another chunk," my husband says.
"There's plenty more."
    Yes, there's plenty more.
Preserving another bite of memory,
I look around the tailgate at the group
    sharing the melon, the friendship, the summer day.
This moment too will last for many years,
the sweet heart of the melon, salted with tears.

KATHLEEN UNGER HART

Moss Roses

Framing the summer yards of memory
I see my childhood bordered with moss roses

somehow, somewhere
each unfamiliar home
yielded a corner for the cheerful flowers

> in the barren strip between the house and walk
> the up-ended tile
> the worn-out tractor tire

hardy and not particular
sun or shade or sand they seemed to thrive
blooming like crazy
glad to be alive

> I don't see boxes to unpack
> old furniture to rearrange
> new friends to make

I see our mother
moving from house to house
leaving a trail of moss roses in her wake.

KATHLEEN UNGER HART

Maquoketa River Farm

It's nineteen fifty-six or fifty-seven
      Judging by our sizes—we four kids
Smiling from under fur-lined snowsuit hoods,
      Gathered from play to line up for the lens.
That would make it Jackson County, Iowa—
      Andrew, Bellevue, the farmhouse near Lamotte—
Seven different houses in six years—
      Still, I should remember the porch, the yard.
On the back in my mother's graceful print
      Is the clue: "Maquoketa River farm."
The place we almost owned but never lived,
      The farm rented with an option to buy.
The memories come back, like a slide show,
      Bright, single, sharp: the old farmhouse and barn,
The river, shining beyond the plowed field,
      Cottonwood fluff like a mist in the air,
The prints of deer in the mud by the creek—
      Amazing to own the land where wild deer walked—
Watercress in a spring-fed pool,
      Gallons of berries from the bank by the bridge,
Sugared and frozen to keep forever;
My father, man of a thousand options,
      Looking back decades later, telling me,
      "Of all the places we lived, all the moves we made,
      That was the place I wish we would have stayed."

CAROL HETZLER

1964 with the Reverse Beverly Hillbillies

The year 1964 was a tough one. Actually, I should back up to the previous two years. My dad held a position in the Aeronautics Division at the Convair Aerospace Engineering and Manufacturing firm for ten years, while my mother worked in the Astronautic Division for a few years less. Then came the big layoff when the government gave their contract to Lockheed in Los Angeles. My dad was offered a chance to keep his job if we relocated to L.A., which is what his friend chose to do. We visited them once after they moved. My farm-raised parents were unimpressed with the traffic congestion, crowded houses, and the eye-burning smog. Why would we want to move there? So Dad worked any construction job he could find, and when those projects ended, he went on unemployment.

Then Grandpa and Grandma Jarrard visited. Why didn't we move to Iowa? There were jobs in Muscatine. They would pay up to a thousand dollars to help us move, which was a big sum for retired folks back in 1964. The weight of the load determined the cost of moving and my dad, fearful of losing another job, insisted on moving his heavy tool bench and tools. This only allowed us three furniture items, which included Mom's nearly new automatic washer, her piano, and the high-fidelity record player with its beautiful rosewood cabinet. Thankfully, after the move, relatives opened up their attics and gave us old furniture to get started. Instead of loading up the truck and moving to Beverly Hills, like the Beverly Hillbillies, we loaded up the truck (and '57 Chevy) and moved to Ioway.

We lived with Grandpa and Grandma for two weeks and then found a tenant farmhouse to rent, the only property available. Fortunately for us, the previous tenants left a garden ready to be harvested. We received some canning jars from relatives and bought the rest.

Mom preserved anything that wasn't moving in that garden. She and I canned 75 quarts of green beans, more than two hundred in tomatoes and tomato juice, and many other vegetables, including cabbage. Grandpa came over with his long, flat, grater-like slaw cutter and showed us how to make sauerkraut.

Our grandparents bought us a used upright freezer to put in the big farm kitchen. We were able to store apples, later used for applesauce, and a side of beef that my uncle donated. He seemed disturbed that my dad and brother were out shooting rabbits and squirrels for us to eat.

The farmhouse was not a jewel by any means, but it was roomy. There were three big bedrooms upstairs. My mom, dad, and brother were able to get heat through floor registers directly from an oil burner that sat downstairs in the family room, which had the ugliest light green wallpaper.

My bedroom had a kerosene heater, and I found out the easiest way to get a headache was to shut the door and study for several hours with that running. The home was cold and drafty most of the time. We found several repairs where a tin can lid had been nailed over a hole in the pine-planked floor.

We also found a hog lot in the backyard, to the west of the house, with the clothesline between, near the outhouse. We did not appreciate the Eau de Swine Parfum on our clothes after hanging them out to dry. Our weekly routine became agitating our attire in Mom's prized washer, then loading up heavy, wet baskets and proceeding to ye olde laundromat for the dry cycle. To my 12-year-old way of thinking, this beat helping guide clothes through Mom's old wringer and then pinning them on the line. Today I wish I had a clothesline, as well as the means to can food.

Another wonderful feature of this house was a room off Mom and Dad's bedroom, meant to be a closet and with aspirations to become a bathroom. I never figured out why they didn't spring for the plumbing pipe to hook up the claw-foot bathtub, which they instead used as a clothes rod. Said tub was full of ripening pears, the next candidates for Mom's water-bath canner. On the floor of this wannabe bathroom were two extra rolls of the ugly green wallpaper.

It didn't help that a box of my clothes never arrived with the moving van. A kind young woman in our church gave me some of her outdated outfits, so I looked quite a bit out of step with the rest of my classmates that fall.

As an introduction to farm life, we were sometimes tasked with helping to round up the odiferous critters that escaped from the backyard hog lot. The landlord's hired man would come to feed them and frequently not leave the gate fully closed. It was very impressive one night to watch the landlord's son, barefoot, chase and capture a baby pig down our gravel road! I think my brother and I surprised ourselves when, one afternoon, we alone were able to somehow cajole these wily and stubborn creatures back into their pen.

As the weather turned colder and snowflakes began to fall, I hated going to town and felt embarrassed clunking through the streets of Columbus Junction with snow chains on our tires. Our expenditure priorities that year were coats and boots, not snow tires.

The fall flew by, and soon it was Christmas time. I knew my parents would not be able to afford much, so I wasn't anticipating a big Christmas. I was therefore surprised to see some packages under a tree that my dad cut from some ditch. My mom took the ugly green wallpaper and wrapped presents in it, then cut up her old Christmas cards from the previous year for the tags. They turned out to be the most beautiful packages I had ever seen.

On Christmas Eve my aunt, uncle, and cousins showed up unexpectedly. I told my cousins I didn't think I was getting much for Christmas since we'd had a tough year. My eldest cousin just smiled at my comments. The cousins, though not opening any presents themselves, were very cheerful and helped add to our excitement about that holiday. I was surprised to receive a pair of pajamas, which I practically wore out in the coming months. The next item was a mohair sweater, very popular that year, for which Mom later found some matching material to make me a skirt. A Barbie doll bridal dress, along with shoes, veil, bouquet, and a plastic string of pearls, completed my presents.

I was thrilled with these gifts. Mom later confided that she got all the items on sale, but I didn't care. I was just grateful to get them. I didn't pay attention to what my brother got, but I was sure he was just as happy.

It wasn't until some months later that I found out that my cousins, for either financial or religious reasons, did not get Christmas gifts. I felt so ashamed of having been concerned about what I might or might not get. They hadn't complained or felt sorry for themselves in the least. I feel now that the true Christmas spirit was lying in their hearts, not mine, and I learned from them never to be concerned about my own gift handout. The true joy of Christmas is in being with family and friends.

I also learned that some of the most beautiful things can be created from the ugliest items. I was in awe of my mother's creativity and resourcefulness. I'd like to think I grew up a little more during those, my own Wonder Years.

TOM HOGUE

Memories of My Best Friend

In the year of 1957, I met Jack Myer at International Harvester Company in East Moline, Illinois. I was 19 and had just been hired to work on the assembly line that put together the corn picker. Jack was 28 and had worked at the company for seven years. He drove a forklift to supply the assembly line with parts.

Jack was a small man with a dramatic flair in his movement and his speaking. He was an actor. That fascinated me because theater had been my pursuit for some time. We had a lot to talk about. But it was not just because we had a common interest in drama that I connected with Jack. No, it was also because of his vast knowledge on whatever subject became the topic of conversation. The man was well-read, brilliant, and had a definite opinion on everything.

In the year of 1984, 27 years after our meeting, I taped a personal profile interview with Jack. At the time, he was 56 years old. He was married and lived with his family on a spacious Coal Valley, Illinois, hilltop in a roomy country home he designed.

When I arrived at his home for the interview, Jack took me downstairs to the large and beautiful rec room. Hundreds of books filled a long bookshelf along one wall.

On the other walls, symmetrically arranged, were framed prints of western paintings by Remington and Russell.

Jack and I sat across from each other at a round wooden table and sipped hot coffee that his red-headed wife, Jo Ann, had made for the occasion and brought down to us. Jack's son, Kurt, 16 at the time, sat by the fireplace and listened. His daughter, Tracy, 19, was away at college.

"Just tell me about yourself," I said as I pushed the record button. "Whatever comes to mind."

"So, what do you want to know? My philosophy of life?" Jack turned in his chair to his son. "What have I taught you, Kurt, about hurting people? Do you remember?"

The boy answered, "The sins you commit two by two, you pay for one by one."

"Exactly," said Jack. "And that's the whole game, to survive without hurting anyone.

Jack knitted his brow and thought for a moment, then said, "I was orphaned at an early age and grew up self-taught and self-raised. I did everything by the time I was twenty-one. Ran my own businesses, raced cars, and even went to Hollywood to get into the movies. They told me that they already had an Edward G. Robinson, so I wasn't needed." Jack paused and smiled. "Damn," he said. "Robinson got there first. But you knew all that."

Jack then spoke of finally getting his long sought-after perfect job, engineer in the boiler room at International Harvester Company. The company once employed over three thousand workers. But, after the Tenneco takeover, only 217 employees remained. "They kept me," he said. "Blind luck."

Jack sipped his coffee and looked around the room. "This can all be taken from me," he explained. "But then, everything a man acquires in a lifetime is taken from him in the end. He dies." He gestured toward his bookshelf. "Every time I open a book, I realize how stupid I am. Knowledge is the only thing they can't take away from you. Hell, burglars could walk right in here and take everything else. That's why I keep a loaded gun in every room."

I knew Jack to be very protective of his family, and that Arrowhead Correctional Center for Juveniles was close by. Jack's property was on an easy path from the center back to civilization. Sometimes, runaways were seen on his property. I knew that concerned Jack.

"You have to be able to tell the good guys from the bad guys," Jack continued. "A lot of men have tried to destroy me and destroyed themselves. Why? Because I'm patient. I'll wait to find out the man's game, then I'll beat him at it."

"But wait a second," I interrupted. "What I need to know at this point is this: if at any time you should, like, get mad at me, you will give me a head start, won't you?"

Jack raised an eyebrow, then loudly laughed. "Not you," he said. "You're a friend. But we're all prisoners of the system, and if you're going to survive, you have to learn the game, and know when and how to move the pieces."

Move the pieces. Chess. We played often. He owned the game. I know many people who have played Jack on the chessboard, and only one of those people had ever beaten him. Me. Once. Blind luck.

Jack liked to stand tall with his short stature while he played chess. Being an actor and a history buff, he would put his hands behind his back and take on the character of General Rommel. Rather than moving pieces around the chessboard, he moved Wehrmacht divisions around the battlefield. Jack would dramatically describe the action as he played.

"I see that you're attacking my left flank, so I'll bring up my reserve battalion to protect the high ground." Then he would move his rook. The pawns were infantry, the bishops were the artillery, and the knights on the chessboard were his panzers. When you played Jack, you felt as if the entire German army was lined up against you. Jack was brilliant and fast, and he never needed more than a few seconds to decide on his next move. When he played in chess tournaments, which he often won, mediators insisted he stay seated and be quiet. "One must be courteous to an opponent." So, when playing in tournaments, Jack would make his move quickly, and then read a book while his opponent thought about his move. Sometimes his opponents would complain about the book-reading.

"My daughter Tracy is at Augie," Jack proudly announced. "Pre-med. A good step. From poverty to physician. The next generation will be the ruling class. It takes three generations."

Jack turned to look at his son. "My son, Kurt, over there, is undecided. But he'll be great at whatever he does. And Jo Ann? Well, you know Jo Ann. Best thing that ever happened to me."

Jo Ann had once told me that Jack surprised her on their first date. They went to see the movie *Bambi*. Jack cried during the scene where Bambi searches for his mother who had been shot by the hunters. Jo Ann was impressed with his sensitive nature.

"I'm limping more these days," said Jack. "When I was twenty-one, I had an automobile accident. I demolished the car and almost died. You might say I survived my own death.

"It happened on a country road at an early morning hour, August 15, 1952. I was headed for home after a long night of revelry at the Flamingo Night Club. My '48 Studebaker cruised along just fine. It was a clear summer night and I rolled down the window to feel the air and get a better look at the full moon. It was beautiful.

"Just ahead, there was a curve in the road. I didn't make the curve. Didn't even see it. Suddenly, the moon was gone, and the sky was gone, and I was standing at the top of a ditch looking down upon a body lying in the ditch with its face smashed into a corrugated drainpipe. 'I've got to get this man some help,' I thought. 'Larry's Country Spot is a short distance down the road, and once there, help is only a phone call away.'

"I walked the distance to the front of the Country Spot store and peered in through the large pane window. It was 4:00 a.m. Larry had locked up for the night and he was counting the money and putting it into a bag. I knocked on the window. 'That's odd,' I thought. 'No noise.' My hand didn't pass through the window, but there was no noise. Have I lost my hearing?'

"Larry looked up for a moment, as if he heard something. But there was nothing, and he resumed his task of bagging the store's money. Then he turned off the lights and walked to the door at the back of the store. I hurried around to the back of the store to meet him. Larry opened the door and stepped outside. 'Larry, there's a guy layin' in a ditch back there. I want to use your phone to get some help.' Larry turned his back to me and locked the door. 'You don't seem to hear me. I said I got to use your damn phone. Open the door.'

"Larry walked over to his car. I followed along and repeated to Larry everything about the man in the ditch and the need to use the phone. Larry stopped at his car and turned around again as if he had heard something. Now, Larry was a very tall man, and I am a very short man. So, Larry looked right over my head for just a moment, and then got into his car. 'If you look down, you jerk, I'm standin' right here.' Larry started the motor of his car and turned on the headlights. 'Larry, what's goin' on? Tell me. Come on, damn it, stop foolin' around.'

"Larry drove off. He left. I watched him drive off and then looked down at the man in the ditch. I did not walk back to the ditch, but suddenly, I was just there. I noticed that the man in the ditch was wearing a shirt. I looked at my own clothing. I wore a sport coat.

"Then, from out of the dark ahead, an extremely bright light came rapidly toward me. The light was flashing back and forth, to the left and to the right, like the light of a locomotive. It was searching. The light was so bright that, as it got closer, I could not look at it. I was not afraid of the light, but still, I did not know its purpose, and I decided to hide from it. As I hurried down into the ditch, I thought, 'I'll kneel next to the man, and the light will not be able to find me.' The light passed about twenty-five feet over my head, and about ten feet to my left, and went on its way. Searching.

"I was in a coma for fourteen days at Moline Lutheran Hospital. Numerous bones in my body had been broken. A tin plate, four inches long, had been inserted into my head. After four months, when I finally woke, I was told that one of my legs would have to be removed. 'No!' I demanded. 'You're not going to cut off my leg.' They didn't. The leg mended.

"When I was well enough to go home, I asked the nurse, 'Where's the sport coat I was wearing at the accident?'

"The nurse replied, 'All of your clothes have been

cleaned and prepared. You weren't wearing a sport coat.'

"'I was wearing my sport coat and I want my sport coat,' I said. And before I left the hospital, I had asked everyone there who might know, 'What happened to my sport coat?'

"A couple of months later I found my sport coat... hanging in my closet. I do not know how it could have gotten there. On the night of the accident, a friend of mine had taken my picture at the Flamingo Night Club. I was wearing that sport coat.

"I dream of that accident occasionally. And I remember every detail. You can see the hair on my arms rise up when I talk about it."

I looked at Jack's arm. His hair was standing up, almost straight.

In one way or another, Jack suffered for all his life from the injuries caused by the accident. Spinal deterioration and limping were the most obvious results of the damage done.

But there is a flip side to this coin. Before the accident, Jack considered himself to be completely self-absorbed, wild, and careless, experiencing everything. After the accident, Jack spent his time in a more responsible manner—married, children, beautiful home, and constant reading to find answers, answers that he enjoyed sharing. At the plant he was known as the man filled with useless information.

"We're all slaves," Jack continued. "Like the galley slave. But you can't beat us. Nobody can beat the blue-collar worker. He'll bring you down. The slaves have toppled every empire known to man." Jack smiled.

He took a small drink from his coffee cup and leaned back in his chair. "I've been fired four times from International Harvester Company before they sold me to

Tenneco," he said. "Oh, yes. I can be bought. My loyalty goes to the highest bidder. But the people who fired me are all gone. I am still there."

I pointed out to Jack that if he did have a boss that could fire him, why then, he would be gone and the boss would still be there. I asked, "So what happened?"

"I write everything down," answered Jack. "I prepare. Then, I wait for the right moment. One boss who fired me jumped up at a management hearing of the case and screamed, 'Wait a minute, I'm not on trial here. He is.' My boss was fired at that hearing. He's gone and I'm still there.

"I hated the man, or thought I did. I went to his office as he was cleaning out his desk to pour some salt into his wound. Sarcastically, I stuck out my hand and told him that I was sorry this had to happen. I told him I've always admired him as a man and had enjoyed working for him. He took my hand and completely broke down. He believed me, and he was crying. I let it go at that. He had tried to destroy me and I had to survive. But I didn't want to hurt him.

"The last time I was fired, I told my boss that he can't fire me, 'cause I know where the company buried their toxic waste. I have had no trouble since. That was my trump card. I had been saving it for when I needed it. It's a man's responsibility to always look for ways to protect himself, and survive." Jack smiled again. "And that's the whole game.'"

Finis. The interview was completed, and Jack's character was laid bare. An interested reader can now read this interview and learn about Jack.

But Tom has learned something about himself during this interview. He learned why he considers his best friend to be such a fascinating character, worthy of such great respect. Jack thinks that he is John Wayne. And Tom believes that Tom is John Wayne. The man who can stand alone against all the odds, and all the power structures of society, and with a pure heart do the right thing while he spits into the wind. Jack and I came from the same mold. However, there is that one small difference between us. Jack was able to pull it off.

On September 17, 1993, at the age of 64, Jack suffered a heart attack. His wife, Jo Ann, immediately called for an ambulance. The dispatched ambulance spent over an hour looking for Jack's home out there in the country. Having run out of patience, Jo Ann managed to get Jack into the car, and set off for the hospital. On the way to the hospital, she met the ambulance on a country road. She was able to stop it and get Jack safely into that vehicle. Jack died in the ambulance as they sped toward the hospital.

Jack's sudden loss was a terrible shock to his family. He was a loving husband, father, friend, and mentor. It's profound to think of the tremendous impact that a simple 'peek at the moon' can have on a man. Life is fragile.

I knew Jack well and loved the fellow actor for his zest for life. And I consider him to be the most decent man I have ever met. I was honored to be counted among his friends. Not a simple man, but I believe if he were here to write his own ending to this interview, he might write something simple. Like, "The light found me."

ANNETTE MATJUCHA HOVLAND

Heirloom Tomatoes

On these early summer mornings, I work in our small garden plot, a sunny patch of earth right beside our 100-year-old home in Muscatine, Iowa. On Mother's Day, my husband and I plant four tomato varieties in two staggered rows. We set cages around the tender plants we selected at our downtown farmer's market: Celebrity, Early Girl, Brandywine Pink, and Amana Orange. We anticipate a colorful harvest. Pinching off emerging shoots, I am carried by the bright, leafy green aroma back to my uncle's garden in New Jersey.

My uncle was a master electrician. But in my memory, my Uncle Victor was a magician.

At family celebrations, he entertained us with his sleight of hand. He could make a coin appear from behind a child's ear. In another trick, I remember my uncle's hands, his thumb striking the red tip of a wooden matchstick, the sulfur sizzling as it burst into flame. We sat entranced and motionless, watching the flame descend as the wood burned, turned charcoal black, and curled downward. Just before the flame reached his thumb and forefinger, my uncle would, with a sharp breath, blow it out.

He would reach out his right hand and pretend to pull a strand of hair from a child's head. With great concentration, he would wind that imaginary strand around and around the blackened match. With a quick tug on that invisible hair, the tip of the match would snap off, arc in the air, and land on his handkerchief spread like a safety net over my aunt's lace tablecloth. It took me years to figure out that my uncle achieved this bit of trickery by flicking the base of the match held in his left hand while diverting our attention with a flourish of his right.

As I stand in my sunlit garden and breathe in the warm, spicy fragrance of tomato leaves that stain my fingers yellow, I realize that the real magic in my uncle's hands was his green thumb, his ability to plant and tend a garden that year after year would yield bountiful crops of crisp cucumbers, crunchy kohlrabi, and tasty tomatoes.

Growing up, I visited my aunt and uncle almost daily to play with my two younger cousins. My memories of those days are like fading snapshots jumbled together in an old shoebox. I am determined now to write a description on the back of each and every one.

March. The seeds my uncle saved from the most flavorful tomatoes of last season's harvest sprout in soil-filled potting trays set on a south-facing window sill.

June. I wander into my uncle's garden. He invites me to help him tend his tomato plants. He teaches me to pinch off the tender shoots growing between the main stem and the lateral branches. The herbal scent fills the air around us.

This pruning, he explains with his quiet, patient voice, helps the plants direct energy to producing more fruit. And this judicious removal of foliage improves airflow to prevent diseases and allows sunlight to reach the fruit to help them ripen.

August. My uncle invites me to sit at the kitchen table with him. He spreads a generous hunk of liverwurst

ROADS WE'VE TAKEN | 57

bought at the German Schlachter onto dense dark pumpernickel bread. He feathers rings of a sharp onion over the seasoned pork spread and tops the open-faced sandwich with a thick slice of one of his sun-ripened tomatoes. He pours two fingers of his Budweiser into a small jelly jar and sets it beside the plate he has prepared for me.

As I reach for my sandwich, Uncle Victor raises a finger directing me to wait just one moment. Rising from his chair, he retrieves a plate of fresh cucumber wedges from the Kühlschrank, a single-door refrigerator in harvest gold. Returning to the table, he tips a glass shaker filled with a mixture of salt and white rice to season two wedges before setting them on my plate.

Satisfied, my uncle turns his smiling dark eyes to me and nods. He waits until I take a bite of my sandwich and smile up at him before he settles back in his chair to enjoy his meal in companionable silence.

Uncle Victor, magician and green-thumb gardener, takes in
hand an injured tree swallow.

ALSHAAD KARA

Everyday Memories

Your death took a backseat on me
I remember your last breath
Your smile is eclipsed in my heart

I lie on the couch all night
Thinking of you again and again

Our kids were in my arms,
Seeking their mother.

I had no choice but to hold them tighter than ever.

Your loss is my entire loss.
No mid-life crisis has ever been so immortal.
I crave your love for me...

I feel like I set sail against the last storm of death
With your sorrow eclipsed in my heart.

ALSHAAD KARA

Not Mine

At that exact moment, I knew that you were not mine.
I have unliked you from my heart.

It's so hard to say,
But so relieving to let go.

I have broken myself to believe a dream with you,
In the end, it was just a misery of dust.

At that exact moment, I knew that I was not yours.
I have unloved you from my heart.

It's so easy to say,
But so relieving to cry.

I am free from your shackles,
free to feel my own feelings.

I have broken myself to believe a memory of you,
In the end, it was just a misery of dust.

ALSHAAD KARA

Deleted Heart

Turn around,
As I fall for your heart,

Whisper to my esteemed prayers,
As I extend to you in grace

Throw your shawl in the sky,
And I shall catch it in this hot fire

Capture those memories of my past,
Why did you choose me to be your shadow?

As the next decade hit me,
I find myself writing tombs for thousands of hearts,

Spill the fragmented fragrance,
Let us melt ourselves in this peak of love,
Merging our sorrow as one heartbreak.

I run behind the thousands of broken hearts,
In the tunnel losing my past sorrows forever.

ALSHAAD KARA

Last of Us

Lovers are the best haters,
This is a truth that everyone agrees later

You packed your bags,
Abandoning the coupling we made together.

Not only this, you
Buried the flowers of our marriage,
Burnt our letters of love in the chimney.

Just to chase your happiness,
You released yourself from the disease of desolation

I undergo such shame
I am a bad memory for you

Come back home.
Lovers are the outcasts.
My shadow, let's walk back home alone.

KEVIN KNOX

Future Histories

I'm a fraud. Future building is a failure. Today was a cold November Sunday morning and I had some time to kill before church, so I took a walk. I encountered traffic lights, automobiles, and concrete, all things developed long ago. No energy field protected me from invading aliens—not even from the weather. Science fiction isn't a way to express hope for the future; it's a way to imagine a future we'll never achieve.

I used to laugh at clients as they made their requests. Childless couples wishing for children. The unemployed wanting jobs. Students hoping to pass a math test. They thought of future building—of science—as something akin to magic. One year at the office party I donned a pointed black hat decorated with stars and played the music for "The Sorcerer's Apprentice." It was a hit. But there are also those who take future building as a farce. That's not true either. Catalyst changes things. I know for a fact it can change the future...well, technically it changes the past...it's complicated.

My older brother and I have lunch after I leave church on Sunday. We've been doing this for years. Because he needs an escape. Given that is his reason, we don't talk religion. If I try, he says I'm only religious because of guilt about my job. I pretend our lunches are an opportunity for him to embrace my beliefs; he pretends my silence is an acceptance of his unbelief.

I don't understand how we ended up here. His wife is a gorgeous, smart, sweet woman. I adore her and their two boys. Maybe her perfection is the problem. Before marriage everything came easily for her, which meant she was completely unprepared for the darker side of life. It's not a matter of laziness or incompetence. She cares and she tries. Yet whenever her latest attempt to fix life goes bad, she has this bewildered look like she's arrived at a party wearing a Batgirl costume only to see everyone else is wearing jeans and a T-shirt. My nephews are a mess. My brother's marriage is a wreck.

"You've got to help me," he begged. I could attribute his shabby clothing to a chaotic morning fighting fires, but my brother has always dressed like a slob. When he arrives anywhere, he looks like a train barely clinging to the tracks. He used to be called carefree. In high school it meant he got all the dates while I spent my Saturday nights playing basketball with the guys.

"We've been through this before," I said. The outdoor patio for the café was closed for the winter, so I was trapped at a tiny table up against the front window like a puppy in a pet shop, looking at freedom less than an inch away. Dishes were clattering and people were chattering. Across the street I could see the latest technology toy displayed in a store window: technology as escapist fantasy.

"You've got to help me," he begged again.

I sighed and submitted the explanation he already knew. "Since people have free will, the mechanics of future building has its limits. I can't make your wife love you. I can't make your children obey."

"You think Carina doesn't love me?"

"She worships you, bro. It was just an example." I played with my fork to release some nervous energy. I could have written down our lines before the conversation ever began. Why were we doing this again?

"Then what can you do?" He leaned back, throwing up his hands.

"What can I do?" The fork fell from my hand to clatter on the table. "What can you do?" He pushed a hand toward me as a stop sign. I went back to the script. "I can only do what physics will allow me to do; what we know how to do. Like cancer. If someone has treatable cancer, I can build a future where they're cured. I can't pick the winner of a baseball game or the stock market. I can do things that would influence them, but I can't guarantee the outcome, and that's not what you want."

"Maybe I do." This was new. He usually agreed he didn't want that. "Little brother," he began. He's pulling rank on me. This is bad. "Either you do something or I'm leaving. I can't take it anymore."

"They're good kids, bro."

"On even numbered days," he said. Lame math jokes were his subtle way of claiming he was smarter even though I graduated from college. "On the odd days, I don't even recognize them. A few days ago the oldest threw a knife."

"A knife?"

"Not at me," he said. "I think he was just grabbing whatever he could lay his hands on. But these rages, where do they come from? The doctors don't know what to do. Carina says she hates me for getting her pregnant. She could have been a model or a movie star."

She could have, but now wasn't the time to bring that up.

Plus, think she preferred being a mother, just not in this jungle.

"I feel the same way she does, little brother." His voice started to break. I had to lean in to hear him over the noise. "I wish I had made different choices."

"Bro, I'm sorry." I reached out to lay my hand on his shoulder.

"How useless!" His shout brought a momentary silence to the café along with judging, narrow-eyed stares. The hum returned. A waitress passed by with a sizzling skillet, leaving an aromatic trail of steak, onions, and peppers. "What good is it to use future building to cure cancer when we know how to cure cancer at one-tenth the cost?"

"No surgery? No chemo? I think it's worth it," I said.

He growled and waved me off.

I took the keys to my apartment from my pocket and placed them on the table, giving them a little shove toward my brother. "I'll watch the boys. Get some rest."

He stared at the keys for a moment, then shook himself. "Always the saint, aren't you?" I read something dark and angry in his eyes. He grabbed the keys and was gone.

I remained at the tiny table for a few minutes after paying the bill. Then, with one last determined swallow of my beer, I rose and left the café.

The chill wind outside seemed a remnant of my brother's departure. He lived within walking distance of the café, but off the main road. A collection of remodeled Victorian homes sat up a slight bluff overlooking rows of apartment buildings and then the commercial district of the city. Their house looked like a holiday painting. A brick front porch with white columns rose two and a half stories to a series of jutting eaves. Tall pine trees nested cozily against the sides and a brick sidewalk was lined with lilies. An idle tricycle resting by the porch announced the presence of children.

Inside was a different story. The foyer was an introduction to a house that needed intervention. The wallpaper bore streaks of crayon. The smell of past due laundry mixed with spoiled food, and it was hard to tell which was which. The furniture didn't offer a single clear space for sitting. Everything was dead silent.

"Hello?" I called up the stairs. No one answered.

A thump sounded, and not a healthy one. Then I heard footsteps and Carina appeared. As always, her fashion sense remained undisturbed by the chaos of her dwelling. Her shoes, leggings, skirt, and blouse were all color-coordinated and her red hair was perfectly in place. Her face showed signs of tear stains, but she wore a smile.

"Go away with me," she said. The words brought swirls of time, carrying me ten years into the past. I didn't need Catalyst for Carina to upset my future, my history.

It was a joke about the first time we met in college. "Go away with me," she had said then just as she did now. Sultry fantasies had raced through my head as a gorgeous redhead gave me a smile that could kill. I think I was on my way to class, but I can't be sure. "Just graduating isn't enough," she continued. "A degree gets you nothing. Do you want to be a future builder or not?"

I managed two words. "Of course."

"Then let's go for it." She grabbed my hand. "I'm Carina, by the way."

Our meeting occurred on a dark, moonless night outside the student center, but that wasn't the reason my eyes felt as if they had suddenly fogged over. It was because testosterone was blocking signals from my brain to my body. Somehow, after much stumbling, confusion, and yanking on my hand, we ended up under a tree somewhere. I looked about trying to place where we were and realized we were outside the science building.

She held out a fist and I gave it a knowing bump to seal our pact.

"No." She tossed her hair with an amused laugh. "Rock, paper, scissors."

"Ah," I said with a stupid nod, having no idea what she was talking about.

After her rock crushed my scissors, I found out.

She made a step from her interlocked fingers and looked at the tree. "Up you go."

"Huh?"

"I'll be the lookout while you change my grade." She sealed the deal by kissing my cheek. Her hair across my face, a whiff of floral perfume, and I was climbing the tree. A few moments later I was inside.

Security lights spilled small pools of light at periodic intervals down the hallway, and I skirted the edges, only breathing when it became absolutely necessary. The door latches were old and ill-fitted after centuries of settling and a lack of maintenance. I pushed in the door to our professor's office, and it splintered a bit of the trim, but the noise wasn't enough to be alarming—just a dull crunch.

His office was pitch black, and the smell of musty paper rolled out into the hallway. I was hoping for a quick grab of the grade book, but I couldn't see a thing. I crouched and felt my way to the desk. I found the corner and worked my fingers onto the desktop. Papers were scattered about along with the cold feel of a metal picture frame. And then flesh.

I sprang back and couldn't repress a cry of shock. The skin had that rubbery, clammy feel like when your great-grandmother gives you an unwanted hug. It wasn't at all the soft, sensual lips of the redhead I had left behind as a lookout. I heard a slurred murmur and the faint smell of whiskey. He was here, passed out at his desk. It was time to leave. I spun about, tripped over a pile of books, and crashed to the floor. My arms flailed in an attempt to break my fall, but they skidded across the uneven piles. Pain shot through my right wrist as it folded beneath my body.

"Who's there?" My professor's voice bubbled from his mouth. I heard him fumbling about on his desk, and then a lamp clicked on, leaking a feeble yellow light.

I wanted to run, but my throbbing wrist made it difficult to rise from the floor. In an uncharacteristic moment of bravery, an idea struck me.

"It worked!" I shouted as I grabbed the gradebook.

"What?" His eyes were unfocused due both to the sickly lamp light and the whiskey.

"Two days ago, Carina was failing your class. Tonight, I broke into your office and used what you have here—changed the assignments she turned in, your gradebook—to build a future. Now she's got a solid B...uh, C minus. I built a future!"

"What?" He made tentative attempts to stand and reached for the phone lying on his desk, mumbling, "Security."

"Prove it," I said. "Prove her grades haven't changed."

"That's not real future building." The professor waved at the mess of papers cascading off his desk. "It's simple forgery."

"Is it? Is that all it is?" I was in too deep now. "What about all the documented examples you gave us of people remembering things that never happened? Groupthink. Gaslighting. Remember your tirade about my generation?

How we have no memories of our own—no memory except pictures on social media, electronic 1s and 0s that can be changed by a fifth grader with a cell phone."

"I was arguing a philosophical point." The professor grasped for his liquor.

"Do you remember Carina, what she looks like?"

"I'm not that drunk. Yes, I remember."

"I don't need Catalyst to build a future. One girl in a class of twenty guys. A few whispers here and there, and what do you think they'll remember about her? Do you really think I can't change their memory of her grade? That I can't change her history?"

"Sure, you can change their memories. Dunces, all of them." The professor knocked back an entire glass. "But not mine. It won't be that easy."

I smiled. The professor paused with the bottle hovering, ready to pour another glass. His eyes narrowed and he lowered the bottle to the desk.

"Alright, what've you got?" he asked.

Carina's grade remained, but I got a recommendation to be a future builder. It was still the dark of night when I descended the tree again to tell her, but I couldn't have seen her face any clearer under a full sun. I told her we'd be partners. We would face the future together. I would build one for her—just for her. No one would remember her grades—her failures.

"I'll remember," she said.

She pulled back into the shadows until her features disappeared into the tree. The next day my brother told me he had a new girlfriend.

The swirling of time stopped and I returned to the Victorian house on the bluff, pristine on the outside and rotting on the inside. The striking redhead standing on the stairs had just uttered her line. "Come away with me."

"I can't do that."

"You were always the smart one." She turned to accentuate her figure. She was in full seduction mode, her raw beauty flowing down the staircase toward me. "You were the one motivated to make something of your life... at all costs."

Then I saw it. A pencil thin plastic bottle a few inches tall had tipped over on a side table by the stairs. The remains of a blue liquid soiled the white cloth covering the table.

"Carina, where are the boys?"

A giggle came from the living room, a memory of running feet and something being knocked over, but they were nowhere to be seen.

Carina put a hand to her head, trying to push a headache back into her temple. "Who? Oh, yes. I think I know who you mean. They're right there, on the edge of my thoughts." The pain passed from her temple to her eyes as she looked at me. "Right where I can remember them as I wanted them to be."

"What did you do?" I looked about, matching details to reflections, trying to catch glimpses of what was before it disappeared. The pictures of the boys that had been on the walls were gone. Their toys seemed to melt into the shadows. "Did you take the whole bottle? Carina, that's black-market Catalyst!"

"Finally, I won't remember anymore," she said.

I needed to tell her...tell...what was her name? What was I going to say?

"I won't remember you anymore," she said.

Where was I?

My hand darted into my pants pocket, searching like a drowning man for something to cling to—my emergency dose. I'd had future histories go wrong before; I knew what to do. My fingers found the bottle. I flipped open the cap and downed the antidote—all of it.

I awoke on the floor of the foyer with a great weight pressing down on me. I turned my head to look at Carina and her husband, my younger brother.

"Officer, we don't want to press charges. You can let him go," Carina said, her sad green eyes peering from behind disheveled red hair.

"We have to report it. We'll hold onto him awhile." The officer leaning his weight on me thrust his knee into my back for emphasis, making me grunt.

"It happens from time to time," my brother said. "He knows where we keep the extra key, so he sneaks in looking for cash, saying we owe him. I've told him a hundred times he just has to ask. We'd be glad to help."

Help. Ha! There they are, the perfect couple. Both my younger brother and his beautiful wife graduated from college at the top of their class. Perfect jobs. Angelic kids who excel at everything like their parents. They look down on me...well, OK, they're literally looking down on me at the moment, but also figuratively. They judge me because I haven't seen the inside of a church since Noah built the ark, while they never miss a Sunday.

What they don't understand, what they may not remember is...I did it for them. They may not remember, but I do. It was worth it.

Maybe now I'm a criminal, but I don't care. At least I'm not a fraud.

TERESA LABELLA

Fireflies

John wanders the rooms in search of what? He doesn't know.

Recall flickers in the corners of his dulled mind like the fireflies he'd capture in a glass jar on summer evenings long ago. He knows these rooms in the same strange way he remembers those fireflies, shifting in and out of context with his now. Interchangeable and indistinct. Difficult to sort in relevance. Within but just out of reach. Fleeing for their brief and fading lives.

Silent echoes of intermittent whirring bounce off walls papered with pale pink and dusty red roses. The maple wood ladder back chair with the padded upholstered seat of red wine velvet once belonged to someone important to him. He closes his eyes and reaches for that firefly. It hums at the same pitch as the whirring. Lyrics and notes begin to flutter together like wings. He sings along.

Eyes open now, the image forms in the chair. Pink polished fingernails push creamy folds of fabric under a needle driven up and down from a metal shaft in concert with the stop-and-go whir. Loose curls frame her porcelain perfect face. Tentatively, he touches the fine softness spilling over the collar of her blouse so as not to startle and chase away the firefly. Smooth corners of sky-blue eyes crinkle with the upturned smile of lips the same shade of pink as her fingernails.

"Hello, love," she says. "How was your day?"

The whirring stops. The firefly begins to fade.

He sings louder, desperate to hang on to the brightness of her.

Her lips move. She sings with him. Fingers on the cuff of his robe have no substance or feeling. The firefly is gone with the end of the song.

If he believes the gap in the curtain of dullness, this touch on his robe is real.

"Dad?"

He takes off his glasses and rubs arthritic knuckles over closed lids to clear the blur from watery eyes. His unshaven jaw opens and closes. He stares at the empty chair. The firefly revives for one brief moment. "Her name was Margaret." John turns his head toward the person attached to the pat on his shoulder. "Did you know her?"

Melody pinches her lips together. The usual tempest of emotion threatens to spill out under pressure. Impatience at what she could not control. Anger aimed at a disease with no cure. Fear over loss too soon to be. Love for the man who had taught her to ride a bicycle, pushed her ever higher on a playground swing and read the comics to her every Sunday morning. The coach and cheerleader who encouraged her to write stories when Mom and her math teacher insisted that she memorize multiplication tables. The latent animal lover who brought home the puppy she'd begged him for on her sixth birthday and celebrated her sweet sixteen with the biggest chocolate cake at the bakery. The father who had patted her shoulder after every failure and her back with each success and called her little dolly until he no longer could remember her name.

"Yes, Dad. I knew her. She was my mother." Melody takes his hand in hers. "Your breakfast is getting cold."

Bedroom slippers scuffle along beside ladies' black leather pumps. The square heel-rap on hard wood ricochets off the hallway walls and assaults his ears. He looks around, trying to spot the source of the troubling noise. He stops short of the dining room doorway and squints at faces pressed under glass and frozen in time. A thin powder of dust collects on the fingers he drags over a frame hung at his eye level.

Another firefly flickers and glows.

He points at a large woman in the center of the photo. The belt on her flowered dress strains to span her midsection girth. Her feet appear swollen under the white instep straps on her shoes. Salt and pepper hair frizzes in a too tight perm. "She always smelled like boiled cabbage." He shakes his head. "I don't know her name."

"That's Auntie Mary," Melody tells him as she does every morning.

"Oh, that's right. Mary. My sister Mary." He squints at the tall man standing next to her. "I like his hat." He grins. "He's got a nice smile." John's fingers trail over the glass to the petite woman tucked under the arm of the smiling man with the hat. The firefly's laugh tinkles like a wind chime, its shimmering glass dancing in a warm summer breeze. "Her name was Amelia but I called her Amy."

A younger man on Mary's left had turned away from the camera's lens to plant a last-second kiss on her plump cheek. The suit he wore the day the photo was taken sagged in places it shouldn't. Everything about him seemed more mischievous and carefree than the older others. John leaned into the photo, his nose a breath away from the glass. "Is that me?"

"Yes, Dad. That's you."

Melody lightly tugs his hand and leads him through the door at the end of the hallway.

Fireflies thrive in streams of morning sunlight through thin white cotton curtains hanging open and limp around the window frame. Melody pulls out a chair from the round kitchen table. Her father presses his palms on the table's smooth oak surface and sits. Shadows and patterns in play on the wall from sunlit leaf sprouts on the limbs of the backyard apple tree fascinate him.

Melody sets a bowl of oatmeal and a spoon in front of him. He looks down and frowns. The bowl flattens to a round plate at the firefly's touch. Pancakes appear. A generous dollop of butter melts and flows down the golden sides of the stack. The spoon morphs to a shiny silver fork. Familiar hands, blue veins raised under skin thin from age and a lifetime of service, carry a pint-sized green glass pitcher of maple syrup to the table.

"Eat up, Johnny." The elderly woman sets the pitcher next to his plate, returns to the stove where something sizzles. He sniffs the air and groans with pleasure at the scent.

She sings about Irish eyes and laughter. The essence of a brogue brought from the land of her youth trills off the cook's tongue. She flips bacon from pan to plate in a single effortless motion. John's mouth tingles, anticipating crispy crunch and salty satisfaction. He shovels a strip of bacon past his lips as soon as the smaller plate arrives.

The music in this firefly's laugh matches the mirth in her pale blue eyes. "If I dinna know better, I'd tink you'd ne'er had me cookin'." The firefly's hum surrenders to another stanza of song about what happy Irish hearts do for the world. She wipes her hands on a green gingham apron protecting the skirt of her plain brown dress.

Younger hands pull at his fingers with a tea towel. The music is gone, replaced by a tired reprimand. "That's what the spoon is for."

"Belle?"

"Who is Belle?"

The plates of bacon and pancakes disappear with the flash of the fading firefly.

John sighs and pokes the spoon in the bowl of cold oatmeal. "Belle made the best pancakes."

A stranger stands where Belle had just been.

"She always had peppermints in her apron pocket. She made a pot of tea every afternoon. Sometimes we had gingerbread." He licks his lips and closes his eyes. "I can still taste bacon."

"Bacon is not good for you." Melody removes the bowl of what now resembles a glob of hardened glue. "Do you want me to reheat it? I can pop it in the microwave for a couple minutes."

"No. That's alright. I'm not hungry."

"Well, c'mon then. We're going to be late."

"Where are we going?" He opens his eyes and jerks his elbow away from her grasp.

Melody pinches her lips together again and begins the coping count. One, one thousand. Two, one thousand. Three.

John crosses his arms over his chest. "I'm not getting up until you tell me where we are going."

Melody feels her cheeks heat up. Her chin quivers. "Day care so that I can go to work." She waits for it.

"Day care is for children and I'm not a child!"

The list of go-to daily responses clicks through her head. What did she say yesterday? What should she try today? Pleading might work.

"Let's not argue."

She rests her cheek on his balding head and her hands on his still broad shoulders. "Please, Dad."

The fireflies swirl and scatter, their golden contrail disappears in the sunlight. "Oh, all right." His shoulders slump under the weight of acquiescence. "I'll go to damn daycare." He scratches at the bristles on his chin. "But not until I shave."

Swells of relief and agitation motivate Melody as she guides her father to the bathroom. Relief that she won't have to bathe, shave and dress him but on edge that his desire to groom could take hours. She sits on the closed lid of the toilet seat, watching him slather shaving cream on his cheeks and chin.

"Why do you shave, Daddy?"

The reflection John sees in the mirror ages in reverse. No bald patches on his head. Unblemished skin free from fiery red rosacea splotches. The firefly's reflection beams back at him. "Because it makes me look and feel better." He drags the blade in a curved furrow through the leather scent of sandalwood.

"Does it hurt?" The little girl twirls her stubby fingers through the red ribbons holding her pigtails. White anklets and strapped black patent leather shoes cover tiny feet that swing inches above the tile floor. She stares at him, her brown eyes watching his every move.

"It does if I cut myself."

"Ew." The wrinkle of her nose tugs at his heart. "Will I have to shave when I grow up?"

He stifles a laugh in cupped hands filled with warm water flowing from the tap. "Not like Daddy does, little dolly."

"Why is my name Melody?"

He rinses away the shaving cream residue and admires the beautiful child conceived in summer on a second honeymoon. "I named you after the song." He clears his throat. The bathroom's hard surfaces amplify his clear tenor tones. He reaches for a towel. The firefly's flare takes the little girl away. A middle-aged woman sits on the covered toilet, her hair more silver than brown. "I haven't heard you sing in such a long time." She sniffs and wipes her wrinkled nose with a fistful of toilet paper. "I always loved that song."

The curtain of dullness parts and opens wide. John blinks. "Melody?"

The toilet paper in her fist muffles her sob. Tears streak her makeup. "Yes, Daddy."

John wipes his face on the towel and holds his arms out to her. "Dance with me, little dolly." She sways with him while he sings the song he hears in his head, the melody he's felt in his heart since the moment she was born. The dance becomes a playful dress-up game free from the daily struggle to slip legs into pants, arms into sleeves, and socks on feet into shoes.

Melody mouths the words thank you God when her father slides into the passenger seat of her car without the usual protest and angry request for the keys. Pleasant conversation on neutral topics, like the weather and the outrageous price of gasoline per gallon, fills the minutes of the short drive. True to their weekday ritual, Melody follows her father to and through the front door of the Center for Memory Care. Halfway down the hallway toward the double doors marked Active Seniors Activities Room, John turns back.

"What is it, Dad?" The heels of her pumps clack in pursuit on the industrial strength fake wood.

John stops outside the main office and gestures at the hive of clerical activity within. "I used to work here."

The receptionist looks up and smiles at John. "Good

morning, Dr. Turner. How are you today?"

John steps closer and smiles back. "I'm fine, thank you."

Melody reaches for her father's hand. "C'mon, Dad. They're waiting for you."

Heavy folds of the mind dulling curtain drop. The shine of clarity dims in her father's eyes. Melody mourns, helpless to stop the return of confusion. The fireflies die. The curtain descends while they walk the distance to adult daycare.

Melody leads him to sit on the piano's bench. "I'll see you later." She kisses his cheek and turns away.

The orphan with a living parent has lost her Daddy again.

Patients in varying stages of Alzheimer's sit in padded chairs facing the baby grand. The activities director claps her hands and starts to sing. All who can sing along.

John lifts and rests his hands on the keyboard. Fireflies at his fingertips play the notes.

THOMAS V. LERCZAK

Wheelbarrow Blues

The morning was hot and muggy, not much good for doing anything out of doors. And yet, I found myself moving some wood mulch with a wheelbarrow, and it reminded me of a man and some incidents that happened about a quarter century ago.

At the time, I was living in a tiny rental house along the Illinois River just north of Havana. My retired landlords, Lawrence and Doreen, lived in a spacious home across a narrow sandy lane. Lawrence frequently hired a local laborer, from down the road, Bill, to do yard work and maintenance on both of our homes. Often, I would see Bill making multiple trips back and forth between the properties with a wheelbarrow, his face stoic and unreadable.

Bill was in his mid-60s, slow and low talking, Great Depression-lean, and tough as iron. He wore long-sleeve work shirts rolled up to his elbow and a dirty John Deere cap that seemed too large for his wiry build. He was a hard worker, but sometimes it looked to me as if he stretched the work out. Lawrence, a highly educated engineer who designed and ran foundries, must have known this, but he wanted to help Bill out by giving him work.

"Five dollars an hour," Bill used to groan in a voice seasoned with years of hard work as a farm laborer with little chance of financial gain or movement up the social

81

ladder. With few savings, an unhealthy wife, and still supporting a pajama-boy son—who couldn't seem to find, let alone hold, a job—I imagined Bill was glad to earn whatever extra cash that he could.

Bill worked consistently and did what he was told. In fact, he did exactly what he was told, even when the orders might send him in the wrong direction, so Lawrence had to be careful with his instructions.

Once, Lawrence purchased several sapling trees that he directed Bill to plant alongside my rental house. "They go in here, here, and here," Lawrence hastily and absent-mindedly indicated with a shovel, making slight depressions in the ground. Would I have taken the initiative and measured an even distance between the holes and set them in a straight line before digging? Or would I have done what Bill did and planted each tree exactly where Lawrence's shovel arbitrarily touched the ground, even though they were not evenly spaced or in a straight line? I'm not really sure.

When Lawrence returned later in the day to check on Bill's work, he nearly shouted, "Why did you plant them in a crooked line and so close together?"

Bill, ever defiant, replied, "You said 'Here, here, and here,' God damn, and that's what I did."

"What can I say," Lawrence replied, "you're right, but dig them up and replant them evenly and in a straight line."

At some point well after the fact, Doreen related to me the incident when Lawrence instructed Bill, "Burn those leaves," most of which had been blown by the wind near another small house that Lawrence owned just beyond my backyard.

After hearing the story, I surmised that Bill probably thought it would be easier to add leaves to the existing pile and burn the pile in place, rather than raking everything into a new pile. Fair enough. Except once the fire began, the flames quickly grew, spread, and began moving ever closer toward the house.

Unsure of what to do, Bill responded to the situation by running in a panic for Lawrence, who was in his home, probably relaxing with a book or watching the news. Bill's loud banging on Lawrence's front door certainly got his attention without delay. "We got trouble!" shouted Bill. And the two old guys moved as quickly as they could, ultimately controlling the fire before it reached the house.

There is no way to know what words were exchanged between the two after that scenario, but I would not be surprised if Bill blamed the near catastrophe on Lawrence for not telling him to move the leaves away from the house.

Bill was notorious for blaming Lawrence's instructions when situations went awry. And he and Lawrence would argue back and forth about the proper way to carry out a task. On the occasion when Lawrence's way was not the best way, I imagine that Bill felt more than a little self-satisfaction. Over the years, though, I have known quite a few men going through life with a chip on their shoulder, with an unmistakable "us" (working man) against "them" (management) attitude. And Bill fit that mold.

I know the attitude well because that was the world from which I came. It was learned behavior, and where I learned it was at a paper factory, my second job two years out of high school.

A major part of my work was watching large sheets of paper, several feet in length and width, gently fly off a noisy conveyor belt and pile up on a platform that could be lowered or raised. When the pile of paper accumulated, I pushed a button to lower the platform a few inches, allowing room for more paper to pile up. If I became distracted and forgot to lower the platform, the paper would build up until it jammed, and the entire operation would have to be shut down until all the crunched-up paper was removed.

So pushing that little button was an important job, even though I knew that a dog could have been trained to do it and stay focused on the task—unless an uneaten biscuit lay within smelling distance. Still, I felt far down the warehouse social hierarchy. Only the box packers in the mailroom were lower. When a "white shirt and tie" from the office entered our warehouse domain, I felt they considered themselves better than me. We in the warehouse used to joke about them being afraid of a little dirt and hard work.

When someone in the office made a mistake, we were quick to say, "Of course, they don't know what the hell they're doing, them and their college degrees." On a daily basis for two years, then, I was schooled in us-against-them thinking. (At the same time, no one ever said that any one of us could not aspire to more.)

Bill may have resented me in a similar way. Lawrence and Doreen, though over thirty years older, quickly became my closest friends. They frequently invited me over for drinks, meals, and their own family get-togethers, where I met many of the extended relatives.

Bill rarely if ever crossed their threshold. And at least a part of his work was directed toward my house and property, while I, as the renter, was never expected to do much related to maintenance. I also worked for the state of Illinois and had all of the usual holidays off, plus plenty of vacation and personal time. One of my favorite activities was sitting under the shade of a large hickory tree in the yard, watching birds and reading a book for hours on end, probably with a glass of ice water or a beer within easy reach. Many times, while reading, I would see Bill working, plodding along, and sometimes I would hear him muttering "God damn" under his breath. If he looked in my direction, I'd usually wave, but without getting much recognition in return.

One day Bill and Doreen were talking in her yard, trying to determine how her flowerbed had been flattened the previous night. "Who would do such a thing?" Doreen asked in exasperation.

"I know who done it," Bill said and pointed at me. "It was him! I seen him."

Bill was right, of course, and he didn't hesitate to rat on me. The previous evening I was in my canoe on the Illinois River, and I saw Bill near the riverbank as I paddled past his house on my way to a tavern up the river for a six-pack of beer. I returned well after dark on a moonless night; then, following a path up the river bluff along the edge of Lawrence and Doreen's property, while pulling my canoe behind me, I slipped and fell. But because it was so dark, I was unaware of having fallen on her flowers...until Bill's ignominious accusation.

Of course, I immediately apologized. As for Doreen, her anger melted into a smile and laughter.

After I purchased my first home and moved away from Lawrence and Doreen, we continued to maintain our friendship. In this way, I learned of Bill's death from cancer only a few years after my departure. He must have had a special suffering that he kept inside all the time I knew him, never saying a word.

While Bill may have been a difficult individual, I'm glad I knew him during that brief period when our lives intersected. These days, I hardly ever think about him, except when I have to use a wheelbarrow. And if my wife Julie is around, I'll look down as I trudge forward and mutter, "Five dollars an hour."

We both smile.

JASON LIEGOIS

A Writer's Autobiography

After I began a writing blog in 2017, I began a series of articles reflecting on my past. My intention at the time was to try and pinpoint how I developed as a writer. Through the process of writing multiple blog posts about this process during different parts of my life, it appears that I might have begun writing a full-fledged memoir.

I never thought I'd even be able to write a memoir, in all honesty. For example, I've always been impressed with all of these biographers who are able to recall what they did during particular years or certain times in their lives. I admired the writer David Carr's admission in his memoir that he interviewed many of the people in his life because he couldn't remember many of the events of his life clearly. Most of that had to do with all of the crack he was smoking at that point in his life. I never had a similar drug problem, but memory was another matter. For me, there are certain bits and pieces that are clear—mental film clips, so to speak. I didn't think there was going to be a test on personal history halfway through my life. But I think now that I want to see where I have been on this writing journey to get an idea of where I need to go next.

The Basement

To set the scene, let's talk about sanctuaries, especially the ones that kids carve out for themselves. At some point in every child's life, they have an instinct to have a space of their own, a space that is separate from their parents and the rest of their family, a space that they don't share.

I truly have sympathy for children who live in large families, like my mother. She was one of eight kids growing up in a little modest two-story house in the northern half of La Crosse, Wisconsin. How did they manage to not get overwhelmed by each other, in that house?

"You went outside a lot," my mother says, maybe thirty years after both she and I stepped into that home for the last time. When she and her brothers and sisters needed some space, they stepped out into the wild world of La Crosse, Wisconsin. There were days at the local beach (La Crosse is situated on the Mississippi River, just like my hometown of Muscatine, Iowa), the local pool, or even the skating rink at the local park.

I ended up having a totally different existence than my mother or even my father growing up. I was an only child, and my mother was almost the only one of her siblings to have just one child. So, it turned out that we three were the only members of our immediate family who would live in Iowa when I was a child.

For many people, it might have been an isolated life, but it never really felt like that to me. Suzanne Louise Liegois was always there with me from the beginning. Of course, Dad (William Allan Liegois) was a strong presence in my life and we were always close, but with him working in the engineering field, it was Mom who was with me most of the time. She introduced me to letters, and I had the alphabet down when I was about 18 months old. By five years old, shortly before we would pull up roots and come to Iowa, I was able to read the stories in the newspapers we got at home.

"You were just so curious," she told me years later. "I mean, really, you were just a nice little boy."

She and Dad read to me during the day and then at bedtime. Eventually, I would start reading books by myself. This led me to want more books, and eventually I needed a place to store those books. This began my lifelong relationship with bookshelves and bookcases.

When I moved to Muscatine during the year I went to kindergarten, I got my first real sanctuary in the basement of our new home. I remember when I first saw it, just before we bought it on a tour by the real estate agent. I saw the yellow, green, and brown plaid carpet across the entire floor, I saw the medium brown wood paneling along the sides of the basement. I saw the weird rooms, like the white and blue linoleum place where I wound up storing my toys, the cement block place where we put our washer, dryer, and a cement block shower and toilet. There was the weird storage room where we stuffed everything, and then there was the room off my toy room where Dad stored his tools and just about everything else, and I would check it out every once in a while just to see what the tools looked like.

But it was that first family room section of the basement, the place right at the foot of the stairs, that became my sanctuary. There was a green corduroy couch that was the place I rested from the beginning of kindergarten to somewhere around high school, when it got replaced by a couch that turned into a folding bed. It did have enough space for a big (by 1980s standards) television stand and video game system, and it did entertain me. However, on either side of the stone fireplace we had these two massive built-in bookcases. Some of those shelves were packed with my parents' books and mementos, but I also began storing the books I read there as well. It was reading central to me, and those shelves started to fill with my own books.

There were a variety of books that began to fill those shelves. For example, one series taking up a considerable amount of space was a set of World Book encyclopedias that we picked up sometime around the time that I was eight. In the libraries at my elementary school, many kids would avoid even looking at them, much less picking them up. As for me, I would go home after a long day and grab the A volume, the G volume, or the R volume and start sorting through all of the articles that attracted my fancy. I wound up learning a lot of random things over the course of so many days.

Even though I loved encyclopedias when I was a kid, there were some disadvantages to them. After a few years, the whole set became outdated quickly. I think we had some encyclopedias that my parents had from the late '50s, and then got some updated ones from the early '80s. That's not to mention those *National Geographic* series of books on the sciences where the paleontology book stayed current for a while but the one on computers was outdated in a few years. I actually am a fan of Wikipedia. If it was around during the time when I was a kid, I would be checking out all the articles of the day and clicking on the random articles of the day to see what I could learn.

I loved that basement. It was where I felt comfortable to be myself, where I felt comfortable to start being creative. When I first began to jot down notes, ideas, and eventually short stories in a series of notebooks, it was in the basement where I first started to do that. And when I finally got my first desktop computer somewhere in my late teens, I did not set it up in my bedroom. I had it set up right in the middle of that basement, tucked into the side of the staircase. That basement was my first writing room, my first creative space. I began to treasure having it and later spaces in the years to come.

Influences

I'm not sure when I evolved from reading stories to enjoy them to reading stories to understand how they were written. It's a very subtle difference. Many people just enjoy books or stories for the thrill they have for a story well-told. But there are a few people that begin to read stories repeatedly and begin to wonder if they couldn't write something like what they are seeing on the page or on the screen. They begin to read stories in a different way, looking at what words authors chose, how they described their settings, their worlds, and how their characters talked. The idea is to try and recreate something like that for yourself.

Again, I'm not sure when my reading for pleasure became reading to analyze writing. I do know that it was a slow process, starting with the former situation when I was a young boy, and with the latter situation by the time I was 14. Some of my students have asked me to come up with my favorite author, and I would have to truthfully say I could just about narrow it down to a Top 40 list. However, I think there are four authors that I could pinpoint as milestones on the journey between writing fan to budding writer.

By the time we moved to Muscatine, I had accumulated a serious mini library of Dr. Seuss books, other random picture books, and Muppet books like the one where Grover wanted to keep you from turning the page because he didn't want to see the monster at the end of the book.

Dr. Seuss is the first author I remember getting into. I

remember hanging out in my basement on an old green corduroy couch, selecting a book from one of a row of books on one of my shelves, next to a collection of records of those same books. Sometimes after reading a book, I'd turn off the lights and listen to the records on my '70s turntable. For me it was a more intimate experience than hearing it in the light with others.

But I still liked reading them. I loved the pictures, so expressive and inventive for such simple art. They were just fun, colorful stories I loved to read. I hadn't even started to think of creating something like Dr. Seuss. For one thing, I hadn't yet got the hang of rhyme and rhythm schemes, and I also never was as talented of an artist as Seuss was (and never would be). Still, my imagination was sparked.

If I had to pinpoint what the first adult book that captured my imagination was, it was *The Hitchhikers Guide to the Galaxy* by Douglas Adams. My parents gave it to me when I was about ten. Once I started reading, I couldn't stop. Within the first three chapters, the world ended, and then it was off to the races from there.

It didn't matter that I had no idea the book had been an adaptation of a BBC radio play, or much of anything else about it. I understood thirty percent of the jokes after the first read, sixty percent of the jokes after the first ten readings, and maybe 98 percent of the jokes 25-plus years after the fact. It was the first book I couldn't put down, the first book I read over and over. I brought my creased paperback of *Hitchhiker's* on a family camping trip with my parents and aunts and uncles one year; it kept me sane when I wanted to return to civilization but we had to stay in tents and play UNO until sundown. It was the first book where I fell in love with the language, Adams's voice, and the absurdity of human existence. It was the first book that made me think, "My God, I would love to write something like this."

So far, I haven't gotten anywhere near Adams's level of writing humor, or absurdity, in my own work. However, reading him made me want to try, and the idea that I could grow into being a writer was first sparked by him.

There was some transition in my boyhood where I went from accepting the books my parents gave to me to be lovingly stored in that set of built-in bookcases down in the basement to going out and exploring for books.

By the time I was in middle school, I was voraciously absorbing every single book that interested me and that I could get my hands on. By the time I had entered high school, I had raided my grade school, middle school, high school, and public libraries for whatever hidden treasures I could find.

One of the things I realized was that there were so many delights—maybe delights adults would have preferred I not see—in those libraries. One of those people was Stephen King.

My mother was not, and still is not, a horror fan. I was not going to be able to buy any of King's books or watch his films in my parents' house. I still had to respect that. But there were libraries, other opportunities to get involved with his work. And I did.

If there has ever been someone that I would count as a literary idol in my life, it would be Stephen King. I can't remember the first King book I read, but I know that I read the vast majority of them from when I was a kid to now. I don't think everything he wrote was great—not even he thinks that everything he wrote was great—but he has had way more hits than misses, and I firmly believe that the hits are continuing even though he's now in his seventh decade.

There were so many things about King that I dug so much. His plots...well, plot was never something that he was into, more interesting situations with interesting people. An outcast girl who has the telepathic powers of a demigod? Sign me up. Recasting the Dracula myth into an American ethos twenty years before *Buffy the Vampire Slayer*? I'm down. Writing two insanely long books that, in turn, aim to be the definitive apocalyptic thriller and the Great American Novel of childhood and growing up? Sign me up, brother.

As a kid, I was interested in the graphic nature of the material, but it was the psychological horror that really got me. There was plenty of guts in some of the books, but one scene that has stuck with me more than any of those was the one in *Salem's Lot* where the father was so distraught at his son's funeral that he jumped onto the coffin. (On a related note, *Salem's Lot* probably had one of the most devastating endings I've ever read.)

Whenever I read King, I read someone who was in love with the art of storytelling. With King, I gained more insight into the people and country I lived in. I also managed to get a lot more insight than I ever anticipated about the culture of New England. (I still will argue that King should be classified just as much as a regional writer as he is a horror/sci-fi/fantasy author.)

There were many more authors that got my attention, but there was one in particular that fired my imagination with the scope of his vision. As I mentioned before, some of the links of my personal biography have many holes, or areas where the fog of time covers my personal timeline. Despite that fog, I have the distinct impression that it was somewhere between the eighth and ninth grade that I ran across *Dune* by Frank Herbert.

I first became aware of the book right around the time that David Lynch's adaptation came out in theaters. It was considered anywhere from a flawed classic to an absolute bomb by the critics when it came out in theaters. I never had the chance to see its theatrical release, but the reports about the story (including an old Nickelodeon series starring Leonard Nimoy) were too intriguing for me to ignore. With that, I decided to find and read the book.

Well, the minute I started reading this massive tome, I got transported into an entirely different world. As I was reading, I was far away from the hot and humid river town in Iowa and transported onto a desert planet where water and how it was preserved was the key not only to survival, but to the culture itself. Herbert was my first big experience with someone who was a master of building a totally different and unique world, one that didn't match with the one I lived in or others I had heard of, but it at least rhymed with it.

What I learned from Herbert was this: the less familiar your surroundings are, the more you have to show the reader how it works. The stories and books that I've written up to this point have been based in the modern American world, with not too much need for explanation. But here was Herbert weaving a massive universe to amaze me—a universe so detailed he needed an 18-page glossary just to explain all of the terms and terminology. Some found it ponderous, but I was awed by the level of attention he gave to it. Of course, it didn't hurt that Muad'Dib was one of the most fascinating characters I ever saw in fiction, and it was incredible how Herbert showed the creation of a legend from ordinary person to a literal messiah for his world.

I haven't yet tried to build a fictional world as far removed from my own and as detailed as Herbert gave us in 1965. But ever since I read *Dune*, I knew it could be not only done, but done with the highest level of craftsmanship.

DAN MOORE

My Southern Awakening

In the mid-60s, I attended college in the South. Some have said that North Carolina, especially the Piedmont, isn't really the South. The region, however, had its share of good old boys who raised a glass when the Raleigh TV station played its mournful version of Dixie at sign off each night. Local residents didn't profess unfractured allegiance to nationhood and took pride at not playing the national anthem, as did TV stations north of the Mason-Dixon and west of the Mississippi. Hailing from New England, I was insulated from their cultural nuances and my experience was that the culture in this part of the South was fairly progressive. I merely observed without comment and was more worried about studies, basketball, and weekend parties, not necessarily in that order.

My precollege days were spent oblivious to the blowing winds of the civil rights movement. Martin Luther King, Jr. made his "I Have a Dream Speech" the summer before my freshman year. Now in my first year, and only a few months later, I vividly remember walking downtown one spring afternoon, drawn there after hearing guarded discussions on campus that the Ku Klux Klan would be holding a parade down Main Street in preparation for a big nighttime rally and cross burning out at Johnson's Farm, wherever that was. More than naïve regarding the prevailing moods in this part of the country regarding race relations, I had little sense of the civil rights controversies that impacted the region.

However, my curiosity outweighed any feelings for caution. I wanted to know just who were these throwbacks called the KKK and what were they trying to incite, for surely their message would be inciting and not insightful. My knowledge of the Klan was limited to what I'd seen on movie newsreels and TV's fifteen-minute nightly news. Neither of these media provided in depth coverage of what protestors, black or white, were trying to accomplish. I knew that historically the Klan had committed unspeakable things, but I couldn't imagine their message had any resonance now. As I soon would discover, this group still held appreciable sway over opinions in Dixie. With this limited exposure to the real world, I ventured into town that afternoon, stood away from the curb with my back to a storefront, and waited for whatever was to occur.

The crowd was meager, maybe a few dozen, more curious than involved. Blacks and whites stood unanimated, clustered along a few city blocks. I recognized other college students, but most of those standing there were townsfolk, men in slacks, short-sleeved shirts and straw-brimmed hats and women in flowery cotton summer dresses with some holding hands of preschoolers. There were no placards or banners or anything to show a groundswell of support, or opposition, to the anticipated marchers. Neither was there a police presence, no dogs or water cannons, as I recalled from newsreels. The mood among the waiting people was as if an anomaly was unfolding, not a celebration or demonstration. Onlookers displayed none of the good-naturedness as could be found among those anticipating a Ringling Brothers Circus parade on its way to the Big

Top. Nor did the mood have the grim tension one might suppose would accompany a line of prisoners trudging their way to the penitentiary. After all, this was the South, and chain gangs were not an uncommon sight.

The marchers arrived without fanfare, no flags waving or bystanders shouting as white-robed men in their peaked white hoods peering through eye slits strode past. The lead marcher, the Grand Dragon, stood out among the rest. He proudly led the entourage wearing a bright green, satin robe bearing embroidered symbols and sporting a pointed, peek-hole hood covering his head. I thought he looked ridiculous, though I dared not express this aloud.

In retrospect, the reason my curiosity was piqued regarding this Klan tradition had its inception in the events of the previous November marked by the assassination of President Kennedy. Those of us on campus were stunned. As yet, we weren't politically active, but we were Americans. Every one of us grieved for the tragic loss of our elected leader. I felt it as a personal assault.

In the aftermath of that fateful November day, I waited with fellow classmates in the long lines by banks of phone booths in the student union to place a collect call home just to check in and get some reassurance from my parents that things would be okay. After a brief call, reversed-charge long distance was expensive, I walked into town and ended up at the Woolworth's soda fountain drinking a Coke.

I thought of nothing profound until I overheard two middle-aged men sitting several stools down the counter talking, and not too softly, over cups of coffee. One said, "Well at least someone had the nerve to do what we were all thinking."

As an eighteen-year-old raised to respect adults, I was appalled. I told myself—for surely it was not my place to openly criticize an elder, much less a stranger—that can't possibly be right; no one should wish that on anyone.

Thinking back to that tragedy and now witnessing firsthand the parade of Klansman right before my eyes, I realized there were people in America who didn't believe in the words impressed upon me growing up in school, in the Boy Scouts, and by my parents, that everyone was equal and should be treated as such.

Now, only a few months after suffering the trauma of losing the president, I again harbored feelings of loss and dismay. I felt a compelling urge to leave. As I headed away from the line of march towards campus, I thought, Holy crap! I can't believe this shit still happens?

I wasn't overcome by a sudden epiphany at having witnessed an open display of discrimination. But it did assail my deep-rooted sense of fair play and respectful regard for my fellow man, which my parents, my father in particular, had instilled in me. Born and raised in Alabama, Dad was my biggest influence growing up. Whatever he'd been brought up to believe about other men had been irrevocably changed by his surviving four war-torn years in the Pacific during World War Two. One of the important remembrances I had of his teachings was to avoid "demonstrations and gatherings, because that's where emotions get carried away and you have no control over what might happen. And if they do, it's a good way to get shot by some no-good who was just looking for a chance to cause mischief."

I struggled to make sense of what I'd seen. Though there had been no outward signs of conflict, I knew that simmering beneath the relatively calm demeanor of marchers and local citizens alike were roiling emotions that needed only a spark to emerge. This was a seminal experience for me, profound in meaning. It reinforced my sensibilities and fundamental beliefs of what is fair and decent and ultimately right. I was confident in the tenets of decency which resided within me. The march had forced these realizations to the forefront of my consciousness. Nevertheless, I was conflicted between wanting to do something about it and not knowing what I could accomplish by myself. What I resolved to do was that going forth, I would govern my day-to-day personal behaviors with an understanding of right and wrong and allow my ingrained understandings of equity guide me in how to influence others.

Looking back today, it's a wonder the events of the '60s didn't ignite more violence than they did. Over the next five years, MLK and RFK were assassinated. Ensuing strife was as intermittent as to where it occurred as it was unpredictable as to when, except for the summer of '68, when it was widespread across the nation. America gradually internalized these events, choosing to express its collective remedy at the polls to affect the necessary changes, not enough for some and too much for others, but changes nonetheless. Social discourse became more the norm for providing the legal remedies to civil differences.

I'm not naïve enough now, nor was I back in my college days, to think that everyone suddenly gained an enlightened tolerance for those viewed to be different. But for an eighteen-year-old, fresh-scrubbed, optimistic college freshman witnessing a KKK rally in what I thought was a progressive southern city, this was an eye opener. It was my first reality check in life.

Today, I encounter people who, in their hearts, still believe somehow they are better than those who don't look like them. But I'm comforted in knowing that as I progressed in life towards influential positions of leadership in the Navy, the commercial world, and civic organizations, I fashioned my behaviors and supported policies that insisted others should value each person's human dignity. That Klan rally down the streets of my southern college town almost sixty years ago cemented those beliefs which I value to this day.

DAN MOORE

Reunion: A Short Story

I opened my email and scrolled through the unread messages, hoping at least one was of interest. I stopped on one, Charlie Kessling. Now there's a name that takes me back. I clicked it and took a sip of coffee as I read.

Hey, Dave, hope this finds you in good health. I'm on the reunion committee, its down to just four of us now, and we're planning our 60th and we wanted to make sure you got the word. Not sure where you're living, I know you travelled a lot and none of us hve seen you since gradution. Anyway, we got to talking who we wanted to address the attendees. We get together every sepetmbr, over at the Quahog Inn at Five Points, remember that? Its not a dump anymore. 20 yrs ago, guy bought it and put some money into it and its no longer a bar, well, they serve drinks, but the foods pretty good and they have a party room that can fit all of us, expecally now we're getting smaller. Well, the 60th is a big deal and seeing as how you were student body president, we thought you could speak. So email me. We got 3 months to plan this shindig.

Chuck

I weighed a thought. Reunion? I'm not so sure...

"You want more coffee, hon?" Laurie asked.

"No thanks, I'm coffee'd out. Here, read this."

My wife leaned over my shoulder, brushing me in a reassuring way, and read the screen.

She pulled off her glasses and said, "Well, isn't that a

nice gesture? Did you know this Chuck fellow in high school?"

"Oh yeah, he was the class clown. Everyone knew Chuck."

Heading for the kitchen, she said, "I'd have figured that title would've gone to you."

"Not hardly. Anyway, I don't know if I'm going. I don't think I'd enjoy it, and it's such a long way."

"I know how they are, but how could you know? You never wanted to attend my college reunions and they're right here in Columbus."

"That's because I wouldn't know any of those folks, and besides, they're your friends, not mine."

"That's the point. You'd meet new people, someone besides those stuffed-shirt engineers you worked with."

I walked up behind her and hugged her. "Well, I'm one of those stuffed shirts, dear, and you married me."

"Hmm, can't always get it right," she said, clutching my arms.

For the next two weeks, I mulled over Chuck's invitation while I puttered around the house working on my list of never-ending tasks. One morning at our Hy-Vee coffee ritual, I happened to mention the reunion to our band of regulars.

"You gotta go," Blake said. "Man, I bet you'd dazzle 'em with your Navy stories."

Blake was mild mannered, a retired shoe salesman who rarely expressed opinions one way or another. But he seemed insistent.

I countered, "I don't think that's the reason they invited–"

"Who the hell cares to hear from you?" chimed in Kerry, our spokesman, whether we wanted or needed one.

He was a short, balding man with sunbaked melanin blossoms on his head, face, and forearms, leftovers from his late '60s tour in Vietnam. Always with the wisecracks, off-color comments, or politically incorrect statements, he had a heart of gold. I never chastised him for his intemperate remarks. One, he never vented his invective face-to-face with the subject of his thoughts. He was too kind-hearted. But he'd voice them to us. And that was the point, he was comfortable with us. Secondly, as a recovered alcoholic and someone with manifest PTSD symptoms, he had to get those thoughts off his chest. I figured I provided him the safe haven for that.

I smiled and said, "You're probably right, Kerry. For that matter, why should any of us care?"

Lou, our elder statesman by three years, sipped his coffee. Never much for words, but vociferous when he did speak, he looked at me. "Don't be an asshole. Throw them a bone and go. You'll love it. I've been to about a third of my high school reunions. They ain't bad. Besides, everybody's either old, retired, or dead, but they're all looking for a good time. And the girls, shit, half of them are widows or half are divorcees or they're looking for a good time. It's a regular Menopause Manor."

I chuckled and silently forgave him for his math, if not his metaphor. His unique way of commenting was well-intended encouragement.

I thought about going for another week before resolving to go ahead and do it. My wife noticed the relieved look on my face.

"What's got you smiling?"

"I'm going," I blurted.

"Going where?"

I realized she wasn't caught up in my thoughts. "The

Labor Day reunion. I'm going to attend. I just sent my acceptance and booked my flight and hotel. I can make it for two, if you want to go?" Then I realized it probably sounded like an afterthought.

Surprisingly, she gave me a hug. "I think you'll do fine. I know how much you've considered this. I'm not sure you need any moral support." Giving me a love pat on my chest, she said, "Go, go have fun." Then pulling back, she added, "And get to working on your speech."

For some reason, Lou's comments flashed in my head. "Aren't you worried about me and all the gay divorcees who'll be there?"

"First of all, you can't use 'gay' like that anymore, dear. And second of all," she said, winking, "they're welcome to you."

Over the next month I pondered a theme for my remarks. My first reaction was to offer some fluff about how good it was to see everyone again before getting to the heart of it. I dismissed that as being dishonest, since I'd hardly thought of my high school days during the past sixty years. I believed then, and still believe, high school was a necessary means to my next step, a hurdle, and a not too difficult one at that, on my way to what lay ahead: college, the military, a civilian career, my family, and becoming a community volunteer. Was it an accomplishment? Yes, but no biggee in my estimation.

I abandoned that avenue of thought, though, when I considered my audience. Some of my classmates had been friends, but by no means many of them. With a graduating class of over six hundred, I barely knew even a handful or two. To discount my high school days was disingenuous and patently rude. Deep to my core, I was ashamed for even having enjoined the thought.

No, I wanted to say something else; I wanted, or needed, to talk about something that was bigger than just me, my reputation, or even the collective accomplishments of my classmates. I needed to put my life, our lives, in perspective.

Reluctantly, I pushed through the double front doors of the Quahog Inn, unsure as to how I'd fit in with my old New England crowd. In years gone by, I wouldn't have cared; I would've simply forged on, confident in what I had to do, others' feelings be damned. However, this time it mattered. Maybe it was the gray hair.

A heavyset man talking to a pert woman with graying chestnut hair noticed me first. "Hey, Dave, you made it. Good to see you."

Though I didn't recognize him, his voice sounded all too familiar. It was Chuck. The woman standing with him flashed a big grin and hugged me. "Oh, Dave, we're so glad you made it."

I managed to get out, "Joanie? Joanie Richards?"

What astonished me was how my little used senses—sound and smell and feel—flooded my mind with instant and vivid recollections that the passage of time had obscured. Though sight recognition had failed me, I immediately knew who both of them were.

"It's Joanie Bledsoe now, but yeah, it's me." She grinned as she did a slow pirouette.

"Well, I'll be," I said, thinking back to when I'd seen her last, as a cheerleader for our basketball team. "Father Time has been much more generous to you than me." I patted the extra weight I carried at my midsection.

Chuck took me by the hand.

"Come on, man, let's get you a beer and meet everybody."

For the next hour, I gripped and grinned and greeted classmates. Some I remembered, with a helpful mental push. Most of them I didn't recall at all, but didn't let on in any case. They were, to a person, a convivial group, here to have a good time, a feeling which was easy to succumb to.

An hour into the cocktail reception, Chuck stepped to the podium and tapped the microphone, sending a reverberation to gather our attention. "Alright everyone, grab a last beer or cocktail and find a place to eat, because they're going to be serving in about five minutes."

A low murmur built again as people made decisions as to where and with whom to sit. As I eyed the twenty or so round tables, each with six chairs, my first inclination was to find a seat nearest the hall to the restrooms, out of the way and handy for a quick exit. But my indecision was short lived as Joanie, another classmate named Alice, and her husband, Ken, who had been a year ahead of us on the football team, corralled me towards a table right up front, within easy steps to the podium.

"We're sitting up here," Joanie said possessively. Once again, the toss-away warning my friend Lou had made a few months ago came to mind. As we took our seats, I nervously fingered my wedding band to make sure it was firmly in place.

Dinner was pretty good, signature stuffed quahog appetizers, choice of chicken or roast beef, mashed potatoes, and veggies. The dinner conversation was innocuous as the other five, Chuck and his wife rounding out the table, talked mostly about people and events I remembered little of. I nodded respectfully, not feeling comfortable commenting or voicing an opinion.

Finally, Chuck scrunched his napkin and said, "It's time to get the program started."

He stepped to the podium and tapped for quiet. I paid little attention to his opening remarks as I reached into my inner suit pocket and removed sheets of folded paper. Having given dozens of speeches, I had settled on time-tested methods for making sure my written remarks were easy to read when at arm's length on a podium: large bold font, double-spaced, so it wouldn't be obvious I was actually reading the words. Memorization was never my strength. I'd studied my words to gain comfort and a familiarity with what phrases came next, so I wouldn't worry if I changed a few, inadvertently or on purpose, as I went along. I'd learned that being extemporaneous wasn't my forte.

"...and without further ado, I give you our Student Body President of the Class of..."

I was on. I felt Joanie's strong, reassuring squeeze on my forearm. Thank God that's not my leg. I rose to take my place and shook Chuck's hand. I let the polite applause ripple across the room as I smoothed the three sheets of paper flat on the podium.

"Thank you. I appreciate the opportunity to finally make it back to see you all again. I..."

A cat call resounded from the back of the room and there was brief laughter, although I didn't quite understand what the obviously inebriated man had said. That unexpected break to my train of thought, however, inspired me. I looked directly at the tables of attentive faces across the dimly lit room and began to speak, never once again referring to my notes—completely off the cuff.

"It doesn't seem like sixty years since we sat on the lawn outside D wing on that June day to receive our diplomas. The school administration had charged us as a class with two major themes from contemporary poetry to commence our way into the world. One theme stared back at us from our yearbook covers: 'but I have promises to keep.' Ms. Willard voiced the other to Linda, Nancy, Steve, and me to incorporate into our remarks to the class that graduation day. We were each to discuss 'The Road Not Taken.'

"The import of those words has come back to me many times during these ensuing years. Not so much because of the eloquence of the speakers at the time—which remains in doubt. Rather, the value of those words derived from the events of the years which have molded our lives and influenced our memories. As I prepared to address those of you whom I haven't seen in so long, I was somewhat intimidated by a great many thoughts. I called these 'What ifs.'

"What if I'm the only one who didn't succeed?

"What if, compared to them, my life didn't really make a difference?

"What if they all lead fabulous lives compared to mine?

"What if I'm the only one who is grey, fatter, balder, pick an adjective?

"Thinking those harrowing thoughts made me reflect on what success really meant. In terms of the world we inherited in June so long ago, it was a very scary place. The Cold War was building at a horrible pace; we were learning of new lands like Vietnam; and the inventions of the new space age—John Glenn had just orbited—were still waiting to challenge us.

"We had Huntley and Brinkley, Ferrante and Teicher, and Dion and the Belmonts. Hi-test gas was thirty-five cents a gallon, Dianna Ross was still part of the Supremes, and Elvis was King.

"We embarked upon that environment to pick a road to travel through life. We went to work, to school, and to war. We married—even a few times for some of you. We raised families, we got jobs, we pursued careers, we paid taxes, we built homes, and we consumed products.

"In doing so, our generation achieved a great deal. We mastered the transistor and invented the computer chip. Now we have PCs, smart phones, microwaves, cloth that doesn't come from plants, turbo-charged SUVs, jet skis, and plasma TVs.

"We can move around on jet airplanes anywhere in the world or drive fuel-efficient cars that use an expansive highway system. We've conquered polio, measles, Covid-19, and countless other diseases. We put people on the moon and brought them back alive and watched it all on CNN. We won the Cold War, defeated Communism, and increased our standard of living, not only here, but just about everywhere else.

"Our kids are grown and doing well, and our grand-children will inherit something far better than we had. They will face challenges—greenhouse gasses, pollution, and terrorism. But we wouldn't want them to have it too easy, would we? And in spite of it all, and with deference to my children's and my grandchildren's generations, Elvis is still King.

"So, by many different measures, I ask, 'Have we been successful?' The answer is YES! Each of us contributed to these tremendous accomplishments and now enjoys a life we couldn't have imagined sixty years ago. As a class, each one of us did our part because we took that other pathway, the less-trodden road, and we kept our promises.

"Therefore, I urge you, feel good about our achievements, have fun this weekend, and come back to the next reunion in even richer spirit, when Elvis will still be King."

*

Laurie met me at the airport with a big hug and a kiss. "So, how'd your speech go? You never let me read it."

"I threw it away."

She gave a sideways look. "You did speak. What'd you say?"

"I spoke from the heart, no notes."

"About what?" Eyebrows raised, her look was incredulous.

"About all of us. In the long run, I realized this world wasn't about I, it's about we."

She tugged my arm and headed me to the car. "Let's get home. I think we both need a drink."

MICA ROSSI

Keeper of Her Memories

I remember her smile and her warmth
Her laughter and joy in her family
So many hugs
A willing playmate when I was bored
How fastidious she was about her house
Hand-sewn dresses
The curls she spent hours putting in my hair

I remember her fussing over my wedding dress
holding my firstborn
and the love in her eyes on both occasions
Parties and summers in the back yard
Trips to the beach
Barbecues and Thanksgiving turkeys
And Christmas—her favorite holiday
Her twenty-fifth anniversary, her fiftieth, and the sixtieth

I remember comfort when I needed it
Discipline when, too often, I deserved it
Love always, unconditional and freely given

Some of this remains
within the fog that shrouds her mind

Between the synapses that no longer fire
my mother lives and breathes but seldom peeks out at me
The smile and warmth are still there
The laughter, more often punctuated by frustrated tears,
still remains

Sometimes she will surface through the murk
and I dare to hope, to dream
But the reality is she will not come back
only retreat further and further from all she knew and
loved
The shell is here
but she is on a sojourn I cannot make
lost in the grim wonderland of her dementia

And I am left to be the keeper of her memories

NADINE M. ROTH

Cornfields and K-Mart

A cornfield grew at the end of the dead-end road just to the south of our house. In fact, our little neighborhood, on the very eastern edge of Fort Dodge, Iowa, was surrounded by cornfields on three sides. Beyond the cornfields to the east and south were gypsum mines. Four blocks to the north, across Highway 20, you guessed it— more cornfields. To the west, our neighborhood was separated from the rest of the town by railroad yards. We were an island. It was the most boring place on earth to a seventh grader.

Then one day, something incredible began. The cornfield across Highway 20 was scraped away. A stoplight went up at the T intersection of our blacktop road and the highway. A large cement parking lot was paved and K-mart, in all its early 1970s glory, sprang from the black earth.

My sister and I were delighted, elated, enchanted even. Lights and action and people and products were so close to our sleepy rural neighborhood, we could almost see the red neon K from our front step. Suddenly, the world was brighter and more exciting. We, at twelve and thirteen years old, had found our freedom, our style, and our consumer savvy at the K-mart just a short walk up the road.

We babysat on Friday and Saturday nights and shopped on Sunday afternoons. We went straight for the cool stuff, too. We shopped for albums, like Elvis's *Blue Hawaii*, which was a brilliant sky-blue, not black like all other albums. And '45s like Chakka Khan's *Tell Me Something Good*. So racy! We bought robin's egg-blue eye shadow and black mascara. We tried on clothes that we could not afford while listening for announcements of the Blue Light Specials.

The Blue Light Specials were marketing genius to this young consumer. A wheeled table with a blue light on a pole, much like that on an old-time police car, moved to various departments throughout the store at random times of the day and evening. An announcement from the public address system let shoppers know what was on sale. The sale lasted five minutes. In that instant of time, shoppers had to get to the flashing blue light to have the featured item's price re-tagged by the attending K-Mart employee. So exciting!

On top of all that, there was a lunch counter at the back of the store. My sister and I, each with our own red tray, selected items as we pushed our trays down the rail. After paying at the cash register, we slid into a booth, feeling very grown-up shopping on our own and eating in a restaurant.

Fast forward thirteen years. I was a young wife and mother of a newborn, moving from my hometown in northwest Iowa to the exotic Quad Cities in southeast Iowa. I drove my car with our newborn son asleep in his infant seat, following my husband in his pickup truck with our dog. After four and a half hours of driving, we took the Davenport exit from I-80. I was happy to finally be off the interstate and in our new town, the place we would raise our children and make our home.

Then, with one left turn, we were suddenly out in the country, flying down a blacktop road between rows and rows of cornfield. I was not happy. What was my husband thinking? I'd always said that I needed to live within the glow of the K-mart sign. It was my way of saying I needed to live in a town with easy access to amenities. The rural life was not for me. He knew this.

After ten miles of me fretting and fuming about living outside the city, I spied a water tower in the distance. Civilization! Hurray! Bettendorf was our final destination.

Lots of time has passed since then, and we've lived here over thirty years now. If you've been to the Iowa Quad Cities, 53rd Street and Elmore Avenue in particular, you know that it is a mecca for commerce for the whole region. Target, Walmart, Staples, Steak & Shake, Village Inn, gas stations, grocery stores, banks, and all the rest take up that ten-mile stretch that was once green and gold.

K-mart is gone. So are the cornfields. The irony of it all is this: K-mart succumbed to brand failure and cornfields to urban sprawl. Both spawn of consumerism.

The young girl who wanted action and adventure, the girl whose only connection to the outside world was through the merchandise at K-mart, is gone. I've been out in the big wide world. The lights, action, people, and products are no longer important. Love, compassion, and gratitude are what inspire me now.

NADINE M. ROTH

Flirtin' With Disaster

It was 5:00 a.m. and my husband and I were in the Quad City International Airport. We made it through the gauntlet that is security clearance and sat down at a near-by coffee kiosk for some much-needed caffeine. At the table next to us, a man commented about the cold weather and said he couldn't wait to get back home. My husband, Tim, being the social guy that he is, asked the man, "Where's home?"

"Jacksonville, Florida."

"What brings you to the Quad Cities?" Tim asked.

"We had a gig last night. I play in a rock and roll band."

I had noticed a small group of middle-aged men at the ticket counter. What drew my attention was their hair. They all had long hair. Not just long-for-an-old-dude hair, but very long hair. Most of the group had some sort of facial hair as well. They didn't fit in. One of the men sat on a bench, foot outstretched. I had to roll my carry-on around it to get past him. I heard him say "'Scuse me, ma'am," in a very Southern drawl as he pulled his foot back.

Tim asked, "Where'd you play?"

"We played at the Diamond Jo Casino in Dubuque. I'm in the band Molly Hatchet."

My husband extended his hand and introduced himself. The Molly Hatchet band man took it and said, "My name's Dave Hlubek."

Later, Tim and I both said it took all our control not to launch into our own personal Molly Hatchet concert stories, which I will talk about in a minute.

Tim said welcome to Iowa and Hlubek said everyone was so friendly. He said Diamond Jo's treated them well. I was a little star-struck, but Dave Hlubek was chatting with Tim, and he sounded like a regular guy talking about regular guy things.

I laughed when Hlubek told Tim about the great Reuben sandwich that he got at the deli at 2:00 a.m. after the show. He said that his "table muscle," his belly, keeps growing but that he's 58 years old and has earned the right to have a big one.

Tim asked if they traveled much and Hlubek said the band travels all over the world and is very busy.

When our friends finally made it through security, we wished the band well and headed toward our gate, where we all proceeded to share our own Molly Hatchet concert stories.

This was mine:

The Iowa Jam concert was on Labor Day, 1980. The Jam took place on the Iowa State Fairgrounds in Des Moines, an all-day event that featured several bands. Molly Hatchet was one, and their hit, "Flirtin' With Disaster," had gone platinum.

A bunch of us piled into a friend of a friend's Chevy van and off we went. We had two hours of driving to get there so we left early. The van didn't have seats, except for the driver and front passenger. It did have shag carpet all over the floor and walls, though. Orange shag carpet. We thought it was cool.

The day was wild and crazy. After the last band, we piled back into the van. Dirty and tired, we all crashed. Except Dave, the guy whose van it was. He had to drive. I don't know if anyone even sat in the front passenger seat to keep him company. Good friends, huh?

The next thing I know, I'm awakened because we're bumping through a ditch to turn around on the highway. Dave had missed his turnoff for our hometown and drove sixty miles farther north before he'd realized it. (Speed limit was fifty-five miles per hour back then, ya'll.)

Needless to say, we got home very late. I snuck in. I was dirty but knew I couldn't take a shower because I'd wake up my parents. My hair was nasty and I couldn't go to bed without washing it. I pulled my hair over my head and stuck it in the kitchen sink under the running faucet. The warm water felt like heaven. The water running down the drain looked like mud. I washed my sticky, almost matted hair by the light of the range hood. It was 3:30 a.m. I knew I had to get up for class in three hours, but it was worth it. I smiled and dropped in bed to grab some zzzs.

NADINE M. ROTH

One Piece at a Time

I grew up on the Everly Brothers, Roy Orbison, and Johnny Cash. From the time I was a kid, I could sing "Bye, Bye, Love," "Crying (over you)" and "Ring of Fire" with the best of them. Johnny Cash was a hero in our house.

Recently, I was lucky enough to tour the Johnny Cash Museum in Nashville. I was impressed and a little overwhelmed by all the stuff in his collection. School pictures and other documents chronicled his life from a very young age. There were many fan letter correspondences, too. Back in that day, an up-and-coming artist actually wrote back to their fans! I learned he went from being called J.R. as a child, to John when he was older, until finally he became Johnny Cash.

What I liked most is that he was a writer. Besides writing to fans, he wrote letters to friends and love notes to his wives (he had two, but not at the same time), and he wrote music. I mean, he wrote a lot of music.

Those hand-written pages pulled me through the museum. I know I missed some other cool stuff because I spent all my time, nose to glass, reading his work. Words must have just poured out of him because most of the creative works had very few crossed out words or sections; there were few caret insertions as well. I took only one picture, to my deep regret. It was of a writing exercise from 1999. I love it because even great talents need to work to keep the muse alive.

The song "One Piece at a Time" is still a favorite of mine. It's a silly, fun song, the type Johnny Cash rarely did. It's about an auto worker who steals parts from the factory over a twenty or so year period and builds his own car from all the parts he's yanked.

Like Johnny Cash's creative process, or any goal we have in mind, we all have to take it just one piece at a time. Just one. I can do just one. You can do just one, too, right? Then keep adding to that one. That's how to get it done.

One piece at a time.

Rest in peace, Johnny Cash.

MISTY URBAN

Kristina and the Blue Shirt

It's 2020, the crummiest year on record for just about everyone, and I'm washing dishes at the sink of my home in a little Midwest town safe from the virus, safe from the wildfires, safe from all but the ads coming to my mailbox every day from a toxic election cycle. My husband is off coaching the kids' soccer practice after we lectured them at dinner about eating the soup I made, warm soup on a cold fall day while one in five children in this country faces food insecurity, and it always feels like a moral grey area, I think as I wash the dishes, how much to tell our young children about wildfires, acts of genocide and terror, how deeply unfair our political justice system seems to be flipping, but then again if we're asking them to wear a mask and take their temperature before school every day they already know there are dangers in the world from which I can't protect them.

And then that Cranberries song comes on and I think of you as I always do when I hear the Cranberries. Usually I think "damn you, Kristina" or "still miss you, Kristina" but tonight I think of 1993, the year that song was everywhere on the radio, the year everything was possible for us as we graduated and headed off to college. You liked "Linger" and I still remember shopping for Christmas gifts the night before the call, which I guess would have been the night you died, and I saw the Cranberries CD face out in the store and thought "I should buy that for Kristina" and then somehow—a pause—I thought, "Wait and see if she has it, have Shannon look over her CD collection," Shannon being at your college while I was at mine. I'd been to your college, visiting that one weekend, and I came to your dorm room as a group of us were getting ready to go out dancing and you were debating over the blue silk shirt, should you wear it, what if it sticks to you, what if it shows sweat, but you'd sewn it yourself and you liked it, and I hope I said something like, wow that's a great shirt, if it makes you happy wear it, you look gorgeous—you know, the kind of thing when you look back later is what you hope you said to someone you love when it will turn out to be the last time you saw them.

You wrote me letters—we wrote letters back in 1993, email barely existed, and we both had a phone in our dorm rooms but there was a charge for long distance so we wrote letters, long letters–and in the margins of one of yours you drew a stick man with his head in a lake and an arrow with the label "Dave," and I hope as we stood in your room with the blue silk shirt I said we're done with Dave now, it's time to go dancing. You wore red lipstick and your hair long and straight like you always did, so soft and shiny and straight your hair, always, the only time I ever saw you curl it was for the Miss Wisconsin Rapids pageant.

And we had a great time dancing, though I don't recall much, just your roommate's really long blonde hair and you laughing in that blue shirt. You loved blue. You wore a blue tank for the swimsuit competition, posing in the pool of the Mead Hotel in that feature the *Daily Tribune* did on the pageant contestants. Your blue denim jacket in the pictures I have of you from Class Reunion Zero, the night we stayed awake all night in the high school cafeteria playing Trivial Pursuit with Steve and Charlie, Steve the guy I had a crush on at the time and Charlie the class smartypants who beat us both with the top grade-point, winning first valedictorian while I was second and you were—three? Four?

I can't remember now. I can't remember what you wanted to major in. I remember the day you came to German class and told me you'd started corresponding with your birth parents back in Korea and now you were learning Korean and German too, you'd sketch characters in the margins of our worksheets, teaching me. You were always teaching me. You were always laughing—even frustrated, you'd laugh, and that laugh was what I caught in the picture from Class Reunion Zero, that laugh is what I remember of that night dancing, carefree college students driving to and from the dance in the quiet dark car with the Cranberries crooning *do you have to let it linger.*

It's dark in my dorm room the night Shannon calls. I'll wonder later who split up the call list, who had to make that decision, and when she tells me I say what? No. Yes. It's early December. It's cold. It had already snowed that night we went dancing. You rolled up the car window. You shut the garage door. You turned the car on, and in the heat you fell asleep and that is why you looked so at peace in your casket in the blue silk shirt, like you were simply sleeping, your face so quiet without laughter or the crinkled eyes, and they had the wrong lipstick, not your favorite red. That felt like the worst wrong among all the others.

My roommate knew you, not well, but she was very courteous while I walked around the rest of the semester like a calf led to slaughter not killed by the blow to the head, only stunned to its knees, fogged with questions.

Who had you talked to? we asked each other. Who knew you were going to do this? Which of us could have stopped you? I saved myself $13.95 because if I'd had that Cranberries CD I would have smashed it, taken a hammer to the plastic, ground the brittle disc into dust. None of us knew why. None of us saw this coming. My teachers too were courteous as I groped through finals though my dance teacher read an article and said is this your friend and in my fog I thought how did she know you, was it because you were both Asian, but it was because you were Miss Wisconsin Rapids that merited an article, Miss Wisconsin Rapids dies and someone had to take up the crown, your duties. Who could possibly live up to you?

Your sister gave the eulogy at your funeral and it was eloquent and gracious and beautiful, like her, like you, and I don't remember a word of it because I was thinking the whole time *oh my god that's her sister, how can she do that? I never could*, and I didn't, when it was my turn—the pastor read my letter to my sister–but at your visitation I saw one of the cheerleaders check her makeup in the mirror at the funeral home and I thought *are you kidding me if your mascara's not running right now there's something wrong with you.*

I can't remember much from those hours in German class working through exercises, the hours rehearsing for Golden Strings, what we talked about all night at Class Reunion Zero, the long long letters we wrote back and forth; they're autumn leaves blown by the wind.

But every year on December 6 I feel heavy and tired and it takes me a while to remember why—the day you died, the day I really lost you—and I remember that betrayal, that rejection, that hurt that our friendship wasn't enough to live for—no one loved you enough to make you want to stay. No explanation. No goodbye.

For so long I was simply furious, a raw pain more about me than about you, and for a while I would taunt you: *see what you're missing?* But now, all these years later, when I have a house and kids and a red cast iron Dutch oven for soup—things my 1993 self never imagined for me, not an inkling—I understand better my dance teacher shaking her head and saying, "oh, that's such a shame." At the time I wanted to say what on earth are you talking about, this isn't a shame, this is catastrophic, this is an extinction-level event. But now that I'm her age there have been more extinctions, and I too am a college teacher and I too have had students come to me eyes wild and stunned saying a friend just died or killed themselves or threatened to kill themselves and is in the psych ward now or in recovery and I say go, come back when you're ready, just come back safe and in one piece, please. And I look around at 2020 and its devastation and Kristina, you're missing this, and I still miss you, and the world is turning again toward dark, toward winter, and here I am, still standing among it all. And I don't have any words to say what that means.

*

I couldn't tell you precisely why I want to relive it all again, but this time I sort through my old journals, the boxes of them I've carted from college to college and house to house, and there it is, 1993, December 7, and the days after, the trip home, your wake, the funeral. We gathered for dinner at Country Kitchen afterwards, a table full of us, our own celebration of life, but I'm knocked on the head all over again when I read what I wrote about your funeral.

The shirt wasn't blue silk. It was red. Red as cranberries, red as luck, red as my Dutch oven. The same shade as your favorite lipstick.

At least I was right about the lipstick: they didn't have you in your favorite shade.

The grief stays with me, building its channels and swamps, and yet I didn't remember you wore that red shirt dancing. I put you in blue. And I wonder what else I've lost as the details fade and diminish, because all I have left now are the memories and not even those linger, though they feel more real than anything else.

MISTY URBAN

Dear Mrs. Timm

Dear Mrs. Timm,

I opened a box that I haven't looked at in a long time and in it, at the bottom, was the journal you gave me as a high school graduation gift.

Mrs. Timm, the things I imagined I would write in that journal! I have carried this box with me through every move, to college, to every job. I have carried this journal to my marriage and all the moves and upheaval there. I have carried this journal with me for thirty years, one of the longest relationships of my life—longer than all of my work and college and mom friendships, longer than my marriage—and what should I make of that, Mrs. Timm?

You knew I loved to write, even in middle school, when you first knew me, I identified myself that way, I am a writer, that is who I am, how I was born and made. The man on the writing panel for college students the other day thought that was odd and very outside his experience, to use the words not as a task or a job, *I write books*, but as an identity, I want to say vocation—*I am a writer*—but then again, maybe he was not born the same way, with stories in his head.

Certainly that is what this beautiful leather-bound journal was for, very fine leather, perhaps calf leather, though I would not know the difference; a lovely light caramel color, with a silk ribbon sewn in as a bookmark, and the paper smooth and white as toothpaste, thick soft

paper like that made at the paper mill where I worked after the summer I graduated to raise money for college.

I am not perturbed if it actually is calf leather. You
lived down the road from us, Mrs. Timm, you knew I
grew up on a farm, only a hobby farm it is true, not like
the working dairy farm across the street or the fields that
surrounded our house as they surrounded your house farther down our road, down that long driveway behind its
hedgerow of trees. We were both surrounded by fields
that rotated between corn and potatoes, those staples of
the Midwest. You knew I was not a city child, though you
could not really call our road country either, at least not
our mile of it, you could say you were out in the country
but I was somewhere halfway, in that space between the
civilized and the wild.

In middle school I respected you, and I did not respect
all my teachers, though I guessed even then how hard it
is. Our algebra teacher would sputter and scold and turn
red in the face, my ninth grade math teacher would simply sneer at us, and my science teacher, Mrs. Casperson,
who was my other favorite–she was the one who had a
female roommate, Ms. Simone–she would simply wait
with her head tilted until we settled, but I don't think you
ever had to scold our class, Mrs. Timm, I think we all
knew to listen to you. Or perhaps because Business
Communication was an elective and we all wanted to
learn business communication.

There was only that one time I ever got less than a perfect score in your class, Mrs. Timm, and it was the persuasive speech, you told us to leave the audience with
what we wanted them to do as the very last thing, and I
had a very persuasive last line, I am certain, but then I
said "thank you" and you marked me a point off because
my last line wasn't what I wanted my audience to do but I

still say thank you, Mrs. Timm, at the end of every speech, every workshop, every class. I thank the people who spend their time with me because time is our most valuable possession, isn't it, Mrs. Timm?

And you spent so much time with me, running our FBLA meetings, helping me prepare for competitions, finding me grammar books to read, giving me sample tests, which I passed, and then giving me the regional test, which I passed, and then taking me to the state competition, where I scored high enough to go to nationals, and you took a week out of your summer, Mrs. Timm—and our town, our bit of farm country is very beautiful in summer, greens of every color, the full streams, that thick blue summer sky—but you went with me to Washington, D.C., Mrs. Timm—if I recall we took the train?—and you were such a pleasant chaperone, so tidy, you put on makeup and curled your hair each day the way my mother did not, you wore pantyhose and heels all the time and a business jacket and skirt, your teaching outfit, even in summer.

I already loved museums and old things and new cities, Mrs. Timm, but that week in Washington, D.C. was memorable. A hotel room, with two beds, and you were such a pleasant chaperone you did not snore, and on the 4th of July we had a spot on the green beneath the Washington Monument and we watched fireworks that went on for hours, so much grander than any fireworks I had ever seen, and I said to myself "I will never forget this" and yet I have forgotten so much, Mrs. Timm. I don't recall a single person I met at that conference, I don't remember what I placed—in those days I was good enough to get to the national level but not be the top, and that has been true all of my life, except perhaps in my writing, where I never have seemed to get to the national level yet, perhaps I have not been practicing enough or have not taken the right test. I do remember the fireworks.

When I opened the journal, I saw I had placed another treasure within it, my autographed photograph of the actor Harrison Ford, my favorite actor during my girlhood, my celebrity crush. The photograph got a little crinkled in my college moves so I must have put it in your journal for safekeeping, because it was a very handsome picture—Harrison Ford in his Indiana Jones persona, bullwhip coiled over his shoulder, a naked shoulder because he was not wearing a shirt.

I was struck when I rediscovered that picture by how much I had admired that jaw, that very strong and masculine face, but I always felt a little embarrassed that he was shirtless because it was a very sexy photograph and having it taped to my college dorm room might suggest I was having unruly fantasies when I knew my limits, I knew a famous actor like Harrison Ford was not for me.

And a beautiful pristine leather-bound journal, I must have felt, was too good for my thoughts, because I have to tell you, Mrs. Timm, when I opened that box and then opened your journal, I was shocked to see that I hadn't written a thing in it. I have been saving it because it is so beautiful, with (we'll call it calf) leather binding and the shimmery white paper.

I counted that journal among my favorite possessions, Mrs. Timm, along with the autographed headshot of Harrison Ford—he wrote his name in capitals, just like I did all through middle school and still do much of the time, imagine that, Harrison Ford and I having something in common. I would like to have thoughts worthy of being harbored in that journal. The grand stories. The deep reflections. The lyrical strokes of language. So far, Mrs. Timm, my thoughts have been rather ordinary and pedestrian, I have won a few awards for my writing here and there and people say nice things to me about it but we're nowhere near making it to nationals on this, Mrs. Timm, or getting a special spot beneath the Washington Monument for 4th of July fireworks, not where my career is concerned. I'm afraid I haven't lived up to what you, or my parents, or any of my teachers in middle school or high school or college or graduate school hoped and expected of me. In fact I have not progressed to the national level in very much else in my life, Mrs. Timm. I fear I have let you down.

I am going to keep this journal though, Mrs. Timm. I have in fact taken it out of its box and put it in a stack of beautiful journals, other beautiful gifts I value that friends have given me over the years. Someday, Mrs. Timm, I will be worthy of all that you and my other teachers and mentors invested in me. Someday, I will pay it all back. All of the pedestrian ordinary thoughts will break into something beautiful and uplifting, into art. I remain hopeful, Mrs. Timm, that I will create something lasting and beautiful.

I hope I wrote you an appropriate acknowledgement for that journal, even though I have forgotten how long we might have kept in touch after, and if you even know where I am now. I remember my speeches and your pantyhose and the fireworks in Washington, D.C. I will always treasure this journal. It is very lovely, and the thought behind it lovelier still. I will write great things in it, Mrs. Timm.

Thank you.

Vince

I walk along a road I've traveled for 47 years, a road I've run and walked many times, one bordering the country block that surrounds my childhood home, which I can see across the farm field that has been here longer than I have. Through the hedgerow of trees stands the same solid shape of the house I grew up in, the house where my brother now lives. The hedgerow is different from that of my childhood, thinned by age and wind—as am I—and yet so little has changed of this road, the same asphalt, slightly crowned to encourage runoff to the ditches on either side, currently full of water.

I rarely saw water all the other hundreds of times I've walked or run or driven this quiet stretch of county pavement. Riding with Dad to take the garbage to the dump. Riding my bike to meet my best friend Stacie who lived a few blocks up, those county blocks are miles, but what's a couple miles to a country girl on her bike, riding to meet a friend? When I took up running I ran this stretch from my house around the corner up to the dump road and back, past the field, past the patch of trees that stretches across to my parents' land, then more fields carved out of forest, full of corn. I searched these ditches for the plant identification project of fourth grade, fern, lichen, silver maple, birch.

I lost a bracelet here by the side of the road one day while I was running. The bracelet was a gift to me from

Vince Lamott and if I'm right we were in science class at the time and he turned around at the end of the class period and said "hey this is for you" and I sat staring at a lovely gold bracelet with a thin curved band and delicate chain. I couldn't have told you if it was expensive but I assumed it was and I felt, as I felt so often through those middle school years, tongue-tied and embarrassed—did I even thank him?

The thing was that for some time before this I'd had a crush on Vince Lamott, the kind of moony crush that seventh grade girls get. He'd gone to a different elementary school so I didn't know him, he was new. He had sleek dark hair and a sleek athlete's body, and he was the fastest runner in our class. He had eyes so dark they looked black and his skin was tanner than most boys, a lovely coppery brown color, and his face—he was good-looking, no doubt about it, and I spent many class periods sneaking glances at him while he joked with friends. I don't recall he was very studious, but he wasn't terribly outgoing, either; he seemed more than anything reserved.

Maybe that was another reason I liked him; there were lots of mysteries about Vince Lamott. I heard he lived with just his mom. I heard he was part of the Native American tribe. I'd heard he hung out with older boys, sometimes boys who caused trouble. There was a rumor once he'd been caught for stealing but since he was in school and not in jail I presumed this rumor was untrue though there was still, I admit it, that flash of a moment when I wondered did he take this bracelet from someone, who, but the bigger mystery was, why would he give it to me? Because by that time I had moved on to another boy, Don Waters (a blonde, also an athlete) and Stacie had the crush on Vince Lamott—we would all take turns having crushes on him, he was one of the cutest boys in our class after all, and then there was all that mystery. For another flash I wondered, will Stacie be mad at me that he gave me a bracelet? Should I give the bracelet to her? But no, he gave it to me, and I wore it often, I want to say all the time, even though I didn't know what it meant.

Vince Lamott didn't talk to me so it wasn't like we were "going out" and I had no inkling that with this gesture he might be asking me something. Boys were one of those emotional terrains I didn't know how to navigate, boys didn't like me—that couldn't possibly be the reason. But at any rate I wore that bracelet and loved it and then one sunny day it fell off my wrist while I was running and though I swept the side of the road over and over, that stretch of sandy gravel and crabgrass and thistle, the bracelet disappeared as if it had never been meant for me to begin with. As inexplicably as I'd been granted the gift, the universe took it back.

I regretted the loss and I wondered what Vince Lamott would think when I no longer wore the bracelet, and I considered using my babysitting money to buy a replacement, but I never found anything like it in any of our town stores.

And I never had to explain the loss because the school year was almost over and though I kept an eye out all summer I never saw the bracelet again, and the next year a different friend had the crush on Vince Lamott and then in high school but he wasn't in any of my classes and I never heard tell of him, for all I know he dropped out. But today in the late summer twilight as I walk this path 34 years later, I scan the gravel again for that bracelet, wishing it would resurface. That one mystery of my girlhood could be solved. Or that something of that girlhood, a piece sweet and innocent, could be returned to me.

The ditches are full of goldenrod and milkweed now, the verge patched with small cottony weeds, and ages hence someone might unearth that golden bracelet and it will be as big a mystery to them as it was to me, as big a mystery as wondering what happened to Vince Lamott. As I think about this crush now, all these years later, it seems odd and surprising that I named my son Vincent. Ten years ago it was simply the one boy's name both my husband and I liked and when people asked where it came from I said I don't know, I don't have any Vincents in my life, middle school by then was buried so deep. More surprising still to realize I've always been attracted to dark-haired mysterious men and yet I married a blonde athlete, and my husband, come to think of it, looks like an older Don Waters.

Where are you now, Vince Lamott? Are you out there somewhere, 47, 48, wondering how 50 can be sneaking up on us already? Did you fall in love, marry, have children who inherited your dark eyes and wiry body and remarkably symmetrical and appealing facial bones?

I hope life was smooth for you. I hope it held and still holds lovely surprises. I hope I said thank you for the bracelet. I'm sorry I lost it. In fact I'm sweeping the side of the road one more time, looking for a long-ago glint of gold as the summer afternoon deepens toward evening. But around the corner is my own Vincent and my family and my life, the place that I like all of us have come to making one choice after another, and I will return to it now feeling light and yet full, bringing the ghosts of this old road with me.

ELENA VALLEJO

daddy's poem

flower crowns,
dress,
baseball gloves,

she would have been
the perfect
"daddy's girl"

         too bad
         daddy hasn't
         been there

you see,
daddy slept around
made mistakes

the knot untied
and daddy left,
taking all of mommy's money
with him

abandoned by her creator
before she had even
started kindergarten

she has had trouble
with men ever since

wanting to be loved,
she does things
she regrets
falling for
the ones who hurt

wearing her heart on her sleeve
because
she never learned to protect it

her life wrecked by
someone who wasn't even around

but daddy,
has never been a father
and she doesn't owe him a thing,
not even her life.

ELENA VALLEJO

great-grandma lola

i am often questioned
about the little green shoe
permanently inked into
the right side of my stomach,
just above the waist

they stare and
mutter their judgments until
i say that it's in memorial
of you

pear necklaces, tea parties,
and more tortillas than i could count,
monday, wednesday, and friday afternoons
filled with moments together

making albondigas
in the kitchen
mixing the ingredients
together with soft wrinkled hands
the smell of
fresh mint and chicken broth
fills the air

hours spent playing
together in the sunroom

playing
any and every game
i brought over

bathroom make-up lessons
in that old mirror
the one that had the light around it
and shining smiles
reflected in it

i was
chula, beautiful,
and you never let me forget it

you, decked in jewels
and holding your famous
tequila sunrise
holidays always were
celebrations of love

each sunday at mass
church bells ring
and my hand presses against
my chest
i cannot help but shed
a tear for you

great-grandma,
you are my favorite
and i would give up the world
to spend another day with you.

ELENA VALLEJO

sunday picnic

we sit by the river
dreaming together
as the sunset serenades us

eating strawberries
and having nowhere to put the stems

you look at me with brown eyes
face a sentimental beige

our minds dance
thoughts and feelings
traced into the clouds,
love letters in the sky

cheekbones push against each other's skin
in sweet whispers of passion

evening crawls across the sky reminding us:
the world is waiting

we pack our things
and plan for the next sunset

we are an unfinished poem
adding beauties
each day

Contributors

Carol J. Anthony is a Midwest visual and movement artist. She received her M.F.A. in interrelated media from Massachusetts College of Art and Design in Boston. She enjoys collaborative efforts with artists of all mediums and is devoted to encouraging work that jumps traditional boundaries.

Bob Bancks started writing novels after he retired from farming. He conjured up many of his stories while operating equipment for hours in the field. Many of his stories are based on events that happened in rural eastern Iowa. He and his wife, Jane, live on a farm that has been in the family for 150+ years and is listed as a Heritage Farm by the state of Iowa.

Terri Baustian is a farmer's wife living on a sesquicentennial farm in Scott County, Iowa. She is the mother of four grown children. She worked on "More Room" in a workshop on crafting the personal essay led by Misty Urban. For more than forty years she's been filling journals with handwritten notes on the trials and errors and comforts and joys of an ordinary life.

Mike Bayles, a lifelong Midwest resident, writes about human connections with nature, settings (mostly rural), and with each other. He is the author of six books, most recently *Second Hope,* a hybrid collection of short stories and poetry.

Dee Canfield journals extensively, writes poetry and memoir pieces, and loves blogging about her overseas travel adventures. In addition to performing on stage with area theaters for the last 49 years, Dee has written three plays and was a theater reviewer for the *River Cities Reader*. She is a retired librarian whose greatest passion has been teaching ESL to adult immigrants.

Melissa Conway is a lover of landlocked states, gas station slushies, and the drive back home. An avid roller derby enthusiast with a day job. Melissa's work has been published in *Saga Lit Magazine* in 2016-19, the Midwest Writing Center's *These Interesting Times*, upcoming *Beholder* '23, and their chapbook *Sundog* is out now. You can find Melissa playing Animal Crossing, eating cherries on the porch, or on Instagram @screen.name.generator

Vicky Dovenspike is a member of The Society of Great River Poets and has been writing for twenty-plus years. She writes all types of poetry, which is exciting because she never knows what's coming next. She loves expressing her thoughts, feelings, and experiences on paper and has recently been typing concrete poems, which is fun and exciting.

Juan Fourneau is a lifelong Muscatine resident. He is married with two children. Besides working at a local factory, Juan competed in the ring as an independent professional wrestler for over 20 years. In 2014 he wrote his memoirs after creating the masked Lucha Libre character of Latin Thunder. You can find some of his writing at www.latinthunder1.com.

Kathleen Unger Hart is a graduate of Illinois Wesleyan University, a member of The Society of Great River Poets in Burlington, Iowa, and a frequent contributor to *Lyrical Iowa*. She enjoys open mics, but regrets that she can't slam. She has self-published two books of poems: *Dream About A River* and *Coffee and Conversation*. Her poetry tries to balance old-fashioned nature poems and our modern lifestyle, the personal and the cosmic.

From California girl to eventual Iowa dairy farm wife, mother, grandmother, then a care-giving widow, life has thrown **Carol Hetzler** a lot of twists and turns. She hopes her short stories and poems reflect faith and the importance and humor of everyday events.

Tom Hogue is a retired high school Speech, English and Theatre teacher. For 28 years, Tom and his wife, Betty, have traveled around the Midwest performing his plays for Hogue Theatre Ministry. He is working on an epic legend titled *The Horse of the Nazarene*.

Annette Matjucha Hovland is a writer, poet, and journalist. Her articles have appeared in *The Hudson Valley* (New York) Newspapers, *Ulster* (New York) Magazine, and most recently the *Muscatine Journal*. Her poems, including "A Star for Katerina", which in 2000 received the Paul Blakely Memorial Award, have been published in *Lyrical Iowa*. Five of her poems were among the winning entries in the Wandering Words Sidewalk Competition and are etched in sidewalks around Muscatine, Iowa. Her short stories have been featured online in *The Blazing Star Journal* and on Mary Swander's Buggy Land podcast. Hovland was a teacher in the Muscatine Community School District for more than 16 years. Now retired, she enjoys crocheting and collage art as well as outdoor recreation including kayaking, hiking, and bicycling.

Alshaad Kara is a Mauritian poet who writes from his heart. His latest poems were published in two anthologies, *The Wonders of Winter* and *OUR CHANGING EARTH Vol.1*, a collection of poetry about the Earth and climate change, from poets around the world; in *The FEEEL Magazine's* 14th digital issue, Dec 2022; and in two journals, *Coeur de plumes* Numéro 6 and *Revue Caractère* Automne 2022 Ventouse.

Kevin Knox's first story in second grade was done in crayon, and he's loved storytelling ever since. Though he did a short 33-year stint as an engineer, he still feels the joy of a kid with crayons when he writes.

Teresa LaBella grew up in Davenport, Iowa, where the Mississippi River runs east to west. The people she interviewed as a journalist and met in her work in the arts and with nonprofits colored her future fiction writing canvas and sharpened her love for telling a good story. Teresa published her first contemporary romance novel in 2013. Two more novels, a novella, and four short stories complete the New Life in Love family saga series. Her first novel in The UnMatchables romantic suspense series, *Danger Noted,* published in October 2020. *Capital Strings,* the author's first political thriller, published in April 2021.

Thomas V. Lerczak retired in 2018 from the Illinois Nature Preserves Commission and lives with his wife, Julie, in Macomb, Illinois. He enjoys visiting natural areas; birding; beekeeping; and playing the guitar, autoharp, and keyboard. Since 2008, he has maintained The River Landing blog at https://www.theriverlanding.typepad.com.

Although he makes his home in Chariton, Iowa, **Jason Liegois** has fond memories of growing up in Muscatine, Iowa. A special education and language arts teacher, Jason began his career in journalism, including a stint at the *Muscatine Journal.* When not blogging on Wordpress (https://liegois.media) and Substack (https://jasonliegoisauthor.substack.com/), he's working on his fiction, including his second book. He has fond memories of his time with WOTA. Jason and his wife, Laura, have two grown children.

Dan Moore is a graduate of Duke University and a retired US Navy captain. His work has appeared in the Naval War College Review, anthologies by Writers on the Avenue, the Midwest Writing Center's *Writers Block,* and the Iowa Poetry Association's annual *Lyrical Iowa,* in addition to placing in the Iron Pen contest. His submarine novel in progress, *Westpac,* was featured on "Scribble" on WVIK 90.3 FM radio. His first published novel, *The Last Voyage of the Marigold,* was published in 2022 by Pearl City Press.

Mica Rossi has been writing since she was in the second grade and barely able to form her letters properly. Since that time, her work has been featured in several anthologies. She also traditionally published one novel and self-published a poetry/short story book. At present she describes herself as "furiously scribbling" through no less than three different novels at once. She hopes to have at least one of them finished and available through Camelot Publishing Company in 2024.

Nadine M. Roth is a blogger and author of *The Ink of Time* and *Not a Moment Too Soon.* A former teacher and forever cheerleader for the written word, she lives in eastern Iowa. In her spare time, Nadine loves to help her granddaughters make grand creations and listen to her husband quote movie lines just before the actors say them. Visit NadineMRoth.pubsitepro.com

Misty Urban is a fiction writer, medieval scholar, college professor, and freelance editor. She writes literary short stories, historical fiction, contemporary romance, creative nonfiction, and book reviews. She has been a member of Writers on the Avenue since 2015 and if no one stops her she'll be president for life. Find news, new releases, and free stories at http://www.mistyurban.com.

Elena Vallejo (she/her) was born in raised in the Quad Cities and is currently studying Early Childhood Education, Theatre, and Writing at St. Ambrose University. In addition to poetry, Elena writes for the SAU school newspaper, writes for *LOVE Girls Magzine*, is an editor for SAU's *Quercus*, and has done some freelance work. She writes to bring to life the stories living inside her. Elena has previously been published in the 31st edition of *Quercus*, the Midwest Writing Center's *The Atlas: Volume 16*, and the inaugural issue of the *Antipoetry Magazine*.

Writers on the Avenue

Writers on the Avenue formed in 1990 and published their first anthology in 1991. Since then the group has incorporated into a nonprofit literary arts organization dedicated to supporting writers and the literary arts in and around Muscatine, Iowa. Pearl City Press, their publishing imprint, launched in 2021 to give voice to vibrant stories telling a human truth from a new or unheard perspective. Find out more about meetings, events, and publications at http://writersontheavenue.org.